The Open University

MT365 Graphs, networks and design

Design 3

Design of codes

Study guide

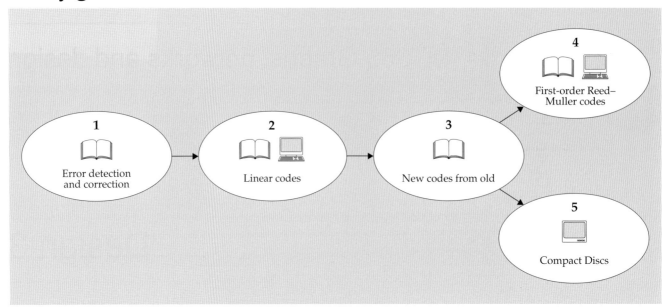

The most important sections of this unit are Sections 1, 2 and 3, and you should make sure that you understand the main ideas of these sections. There are computer activities associated with Sections 2, 3 and 4.

If you are short of time, you may prefer to skim through Section 4, referring back to it later if you need to.

You can watch the television programme at any time while working on the unit. There is no audio-tape associated with this unit.

The Open University, Walton Hall, Milton Keynes, MK7 6AA.

First published 1995. Second edition 2009.

Printed and bound in Malta by Gutenberg Press Limited.

ISBN 978 0 7492 5423 0

2.1

Contents

Introduction

Codes are often associated in the public mind with spies, intrigue and secret messages — that is, as tools for *concealing information*. Such coding schemes, sometimes called *encryption* or *encipherment systems*, are used in political, commercial and military situations for which it is important to keep information secure. Modern encryption systems involve some interesting mathematics, but they are not the main concern of this unit.

In recent times, with the rapid growth of information processing industries, codes have also come to be used widely for *representing information*. There are many codes in everyday use which are specifically designed for use with modern technology — for example, ASCII codes (used in computing), bar codes (used in retailing) and ISBN codes (used in library cataloguing). In the past, much use has been made of Morse code (used in telegraphy) and ICL 1900 8-track code (commonly used for punched paper tape).

The codes in this unit have a different purpose. Here they are used for *conveying information*. More precisely, they provide us with the means to ensure more efficient transmission of information and to guard against errors that might alter the meaning of a message we are trying to send. These codes have arisen as a product of the changes in telecommunications since 1945 — in particular, the introduction of digital transmission — and result from the use of abstract pure mathematics to solve practical engineering problems. In this unit, we consider the design of efficient codes (in a sense to be explained later) and the design of codes for error detection and error correction.

In Section 1, *Error detection and correction,* we introduce block codes and discuss some simple coding schemes that allow errors to be detected and corrected.

In Section 2, *Linear codes,* we consider the important family of *linear* codes, which occupy us for the remainder of the unit. Linear codes are particularly amenable to the use of algebraic methods for the analysis of their error-correcting properties.

In Section 3, *New codes from old,* we investigate the mathematical relationships between various codes, and discuss several methods for constructing new codes from given ones.

Next, in Section 4 *First-order Reed-Muller codes,* we introduce some codes that have proved to be of great mathematical and practical importance. In particular, we describe the code used to transmit data back to Earth in the Mariner 9 space project.

Finally, in Section 5, *Compact discs,* we introduce some codes involved in the design of compact discs.

One of the earliest papers on error-correcting codes was written by R. W. Hamming and published in 1950. This paper is reproduced in the Appendix at the end of the unit.

1 Error detection and correction

In this section we discuss the use of codes to transmit messages over a communication channel in the presence of 'noise' that is liable to distort the message. We show how some codes are better than others in the amount of information they can convey accurately and efficiently, and this leads us to study error detection and correction.

1.1 Communication channels

Since our main concern in this unit is with the communication of information, it is useful to set up a model of a general communication process. An abstract communication system can be represented as in the following diagram:

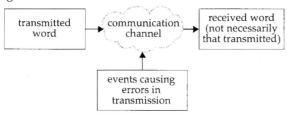

The input message on the left is encoded by the transmitter and communicated to the receiver which decodes it and produces the output message. During communication, the transmitted message may be distorted by 'noise', such as interference or some other spurious and unwanted effect that introduces errors into the message.

A simple example is that of human speech, where the input message is a thought in the speaker's mind, the transmitter is the speaker's larynx (the encoding of thoughts into sound waves), the channel may be the air or a telephone line between speaker and listener, and the receiver is the listener's ear which decodes the signal and generates the output message as a thought in the listener's mind. The message may be subject to noise, such as a plane flying overhead, a nearby pneumatic drill, or interference on the telephone line, and such noise may make the message difficult to understand.

Fortunately, the English language has a great deal of built-in redundancy, so that a listener can interpret the received message correctly, even if some words are lost through noise. Such redundancy helps also with the printed word. For example, the sentence

Matkemadicr is hxrd vork.

is not difficult to understand, even though five of its twenty-one letters have been corrupted.

In many situations, it is common for the input message to be transmitted as a *binary word* — a sequence of *binary digits* (0s and 1s), called *bits* — for example, when a space probe signals back to Earth, or in a telecommunication or computer system. In such cases, the bits are transmitted through a communication channel — an electrical or telephone cable, optical fibres, or the Earth's atmosphere (in the case of radio waves). Such communication channels are subject to interference from sources of noise, and the effect is to corrupt some of the transmitted bits, so that 0 is received as 1, and 1 is received as 0. For example, if the message 0110 is sent and if one bit becomes corrupted, then the message will be received as 1110, 0010, 0100 or 0111. If there is enough redundancy in the code, we may be able to detect that an error has arisen and determine that the correct message was indeed 0110.

In order to do this, we need to investigate redundancy in some detail. We could alleviate the problem by transmitting the same message several times and eliminate any discrepancies that arise, but this would mean extending the message considerably, which may be expensive or impracticable. We need to obtain a satisfactory balance between extending a message by just a few bits to create enough redundancy and extending it by many bits, which would be too costly. So among the main questions to be discussed in this unit are:

- how many extra bits must be added to each message of a fixed length to provide a given level of error protection?

- how do we decide how to add these extra bits so as to achieve the most efficient code?

By **encoding** we mean identifying each possible binary message of (say) k bits with a binary codeword containing n bits, where $n > k$, according to some **encoding rule**. We thus incorporate *redundancy* into the code we construct. It is this redundancy that enables us to correct errors in transmission. Our diagram of a communication channel can now be expanded:

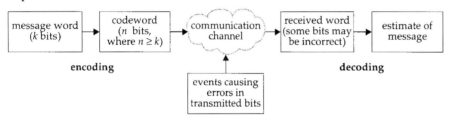

By **decoding**, we mean estimating the original message from the received word. If few errors have occurred in transmission and the code is efficient, this can be done accurately.

Decoding is based on assumptions about the number of errors introduced. Wrong assumptions lead to inaccurate decoding.

The codes we study in this unit consist of a number of binary words, each containing the same number of bits. Such codes are known as **block codes**, because each codeword is a block of binary digits.

Definition

Each binary word in a code is a **codeword**. The number n of bits in each codeword of a block code is the **length** of the code.

For example, consider the code

{0000, 0011, 0101, 0110, 1001, 1010, 1100, 1111}.

This code has eight codewords, and is a code of length 4. Another code of length 4 has all the 4-bit binary words as codewords:

{0000, 0001, 0010, 0011, 0100, 0101, 0110, 0111,

1000, 1001, 1010, 1011, 1100, 1101, 1110, 1111}.

Problem 1.1 ─────────────────────────────

A code is to be used to send all possible messages of length 5. What is the minimum number of codewords that it must contain?

Most of the codes we study in this unit are constructed by adding $n - k$ **check bits** to each message of length k to make a binary word of length n. Such a code consists of 2^k of the 2^n possible strings of n bits. For example, the code

{000, 011, 101, 110}

can be used to transmit all 2-bit messages (00, 01, 10, 11); each message occurs as the first two bits of the appropriate codeword. We describe such a code as a (3, 2) code. More generally, we make the following definition.

> **Definition**
>
> A code of length n, with k message bits and 2^k codewords, is an **(n, k) code**. The number k is the **dimension** of the code.

Problem 1.2

What is the dimension of each of the following codes?

(a) {0000, 0101, 1010, 1111}; 4 ,   1/2 ..

(b) {0000, 1100, 0011, 1111}; 4 ,   1/2

(c) {0000, 0011, 0101, 0110, 1001, 1010, 1100, 1111}. 8 ,   3/4 .

We can measure the *efficiency* of a code by the *reciprocal* of the number of coded bits needed to transmit each bit of information; we call this measure the *rate* of the code.

> **Definition**
>
> The **rate** of a code is k/n, where k is the number of message bits in each codeword and n is the length of the code.

Problem 1.3

(a) Write down the rate of each of the codes in Problem 1.2.

(b) What is the rate of a code of length 7 with 16 codewords?

Consider again the code

{000, 011, 101, 110},

in which each 2-bit message occurs as the first two bits of the appropriate codeword. Such an encoding rule, in which all possible messages of a given length occur in fixed positions in the codewords, is called *systematic*.

> **Definition**
>
> An encoding rule that results in the k bits of the message appearing in fixed positions in the corresponding codeword is a **systematic encoding rule**. The k message bits need not necessarily form the first k bits of each codeword, nor need they appear in k consecutive places, but they must appear in the same order in each codeword, in some fixed set of k places.

For example, consider the code

{0000000, 1101001, 0101010, 1000011, 1001100, 0100101, 1100110, 0001111, 1110000, 0011001, 1011010, 0110011, 0111100, 1010101, 0010110, 1111111}.

This code has sixteen (2^4) codewords, and is of length 7; it is therefore a (7, 4) code with rate 4/7.

We can use this code to transmit four-digit binary numbers. We use the first codeword to denote 0000, the second to denote 0001, the third to denote 0010, and so on down the list. In each case, the bits in the third, fifth, sixth and seventh places of the codeword form the binary number represented by that codeword. The encoding rule described in this example is therefore systematic.

Problem 1.4

(a) Is the following encoding rule systematic?

message	codeword
0	11
1	00

(b) Are there systematic encoding rules for the codes in Problem 1.2?

Historical note

The theory of error-correcting codes was developed in the 1950s, to cope with the problems of transmitting data over noisy channels. Much early work was carried out at the Bell Telephone Laboratories, in an effort to realize in a constructive way the pioneering theories of Claude Shannon. In his paper *The Mathematical Theory of Communication,* published in 1948, Shannon had proved the existence of codes that allowed the transmission of data at arbitrarily low error rates. In other words, 'almost all' transmission errors can be corrected, provided that 'sufficient' extra bits are transmitted along with the data, and the proportion of extra bits need not be unduly large.

1.2 Error detection

Consider again the code

{000, 011, 101, 110}.

Suppose that a codeword from this code is transmitted, and the binary word 010 is received. Since 010 is not one of the codewords, we know that at least one error must have occurred in transmission, but we cannot tell which bits are incorrect, or which message was intended. If we can assume from our knowledge of the communication channel that one error is more likely to have occurred than several errors, then we can deduce that any of the codewords 000, 011 or 110 could have been transmitted, but without further information we cannot determine which one. We can *detect* that an error has occurred, but we cannot *correct* it.

In some circumstances, we may be content merely to detect errors, rather than to correct them. It may be too costly to build in much redundancy — for example, a NASA space probe may have only one opportunity to scan part of a planet's surface and transmit its data back to earth — and so we have to cope with the received coded message as best we can. In other circumstances, if we can detect the occurrence of errors, we can then request a repeat transmission of the suspect codeword.

Example 1: Code R(2), the 2-fold repetition code

Suppose that we transmit each bit of information twice, as follows.

message	codeword
0	00
1	11

If the word 01 is received, instead of 00 or 11, then we can deduce that an error has occurred, but we cannot tell which bit is incorrect. The code can *detect,* but not *correct,* one error.

We paid a heavy price for the slight error protection in Code $R(2)$. For each bit of information, two bits must be transmitted, and so the code is rather inefficient. Since Code $R(2)$ is a (2, 1) code, its rate is only $1/2$. ∎

If both bits of a transmitted codeword are affected by errors, then the decoding procedure based on the assumption of at most one error yields an incorrect estimate of the intended message.

If we wish to obtain codes with rate higher than $1/2$, we must encode messages with two or more bits. It also pays to look for more sophisticated methods of adding redundant bits to messages. For example, in Section 1.5

we shall meet a code of rate $1/2$ which can *correct* one error — an improvement on Code $R(2)$. Thus, a code of rate $1/2$ can be constructed in better ways than by simply repeating each message.

Our next example is of another code that can detect one error, but at a higher rate than Code $R(2)$.

Example 1.2: the even-weight code of length 4

Suppose that we wish to transmit information in messages of three bits. To each message transmitted, we add a fourth bit chosen so that the sum of the four bits is even; for example, the message 001 is encoded as 0011, and the message 101 is encoded as 1010.

This gives the code

{0000, 0011, 0101, 0110, 1001, 1010, 1100, 1111}.

What happens when an error affects a codeword from this code? For example, suppose that we receive the word 1000. This is not a codeword, since the sum of its bits is an odd number. We can detect that at least one error has occurred, but we cannot tell whether the intended message was 110, 101, 100 or 000. The encoded versions of these messages — namely, 1100, 1010, 1001 and 0000 — can each be corrupted in one bit to yield the received word 1000. As in Code $R(2)$, we can do no more than *detect* that one error has occurred. ■

The fourth bit is called an **overall parity check**. The term **even-weight** means that the sum of the bits in each codeword is even. The *weight* of a codeword is formally defined on page 15.

We saw in Problems 1.3(a) and 1.4(b) that this is a systematic code with rate $3/4$.

Note that the corruption of any *two* bits invariably leads to incorrect decoding, since the parity of the transmitted codeword is unaffected; for example, the codeword 0101 might be received as 0000, 1111, 1001, 0110, 1100 or 0011.

1.3 Error correction

Suppose now that we wish to do more than *detect* that errors have occurred in a received word. We cannot always repeat corrupted codewords, and even if we can, it uses time and energy. How can we incorporate sufficient redundancy into a code so as to ensure that errors can be both *detected* and *located* — in other words, *corrected*? In our next example, we use a code of the same type as Code $R(2)$ — that is, a *repetition code*.

Example 1.3: Code $R(3)$, the 3-fold repetition code

Suppose that we transmit each bit of information three times, as follows.

message	codeword
0	000
1	111

If we receive a word that is not a codeword, we can now sometimes recover the intended message. For example, suppose that we receive 101. Then either 111 was sent and the second bit is in error, or 000 was sent and the other two bits were corrupted. If we assume that just one error has occurred, then we choose the former option and decode the message as 1. Code $R(3)$ is therefore a *single*-error-correcting code, and it is decoded by a very simple example of **majority-logic decoding**: for each bit of information there are three 'votes', and we choose the value with the largest number of votes. ■

You have now met $R(2)$, the 2-fold repetition code, and $R(3)$, the 3-fold repetition code. The **n-fold repetition code** $R(n)$ is constructed similarly, for each integer $n > 1$.

Problem 1.5

(a) What is the rate of the 4-fold repetition code $R(4)$? How many errors can $R(4)$ detect and correct?

(b) What is the rate of the 5-fold repetition code $R(5)$? How many errors can $R(5)$ detect and correct?

Example 1.4: Code $R(n)$, the n-fold repetition code

Suppose that we transmit each bit of information n times, as follows.

message	codeword
0	00 ... 0 (n bits)
1	11 ... 1 (n bits)

The first of these words is
the *zero word*, denoted by **0**.

Since each bit of information gives rise to n transmitted bits, the rate of the code $R(n)$ is $1/n$.

How many errors can $R(n)$ detect and correct?

Note that correct decoding is possible only when a majority of the bits in a received word correspond to the message bit of the transmitted codeword. If exactly half of the bits are wrong, then no majority verdict on the value of the message bit is possible. In this case, which can happen only when n is even, the errors can be detected, but not corrected. It follows that:

* if n is odd, the code $R(n)$ can detect and correct up to $(n-1)/2$ errors.
* if n is even, the code $R(n)$ can detect up to $n/2$ errors and correct up to $(n-2)/2$ errors. ∎

1.4 Hamming distance

The above discussion of the n-fold repetition code $R(n)$ depends on the fact that the two codewords of this code differ in all n bits. We now formalize this concept of a 'distance' between two codewords.

Definition

The **Hamming distance** $d(\mathbf{x}, \mathbf{y})$ between two binary words $\mathbf{x}$ and $\mathbf{y}$ of a block code is the number of places in which their bits differ.

For example, consider the code

$$\{0000, 0011, 0101, 0110, 1001, 1010, 1100, 1111\}.$$

If $\mathbf{x} = 0011$ and $\mathbf{y} = 1001$, then $\mathbf{x}$ and $\mathbf{y}$ differ in the first and third bits, and so $d(\mathbf{x}, \mathbf{y}) = 2$.

Problem 1.6

For the above code, write down $d(\mathbf{x}, \mathbf{y})$ in each of the following cases:

(a) $\mathbf{x} = 1111, \mathbf{y} = 0101$;   (b) $\mathbf{x} = 0110, \mathbf{y} = 1001$;   (c) $\mathbf{x} = \mathbf{y} = 1001$.

Problem 1.7

(a) Find $d(\mathbf{x}, \mathbf{y})$ when

     (1) $\mathbf{x} = 11000$ and $\mathbf{y} = 10101$;   (2) $\mathbf{x} = 1100101$ and $\mathbf{y} = 0111011$.

(b) Find $d(\mathbf{x}, \mathbf{z})$, $d(\mathbf{x}, \mathbf{y})$ and $d(\mathbf{y}, \mathbf{z})$ when

     $\mathbf{x} = 111001$, $\mathbf{y} = 001111$, $\mathbf{z} = 101010$.

Properties of Hamming distance
For any binary words $\mathbf{x}$, $\mathbf{y}$ and $\mathbf{z}$ of the same length,

* $d(\mathbf{x}, \mathbf{y}) = d(\mathbf{y}, \mathbf{x})$;   (symmetry)
* $d(\mathbf{x}, \mathbf{z}) \leq d(\mathbf{x}, \mathbf{y}) + d(\mathbf{y}, \mathbf{z})$.   (triangle inequality)
* $d(\mathbf{x}, \mathbf{y}) \geq 0$
* $d(\mathbf{x}, \mathbf{y}) = 0$ if and only if $\mathbf{x} = \mathbf{y}$.

Any measure that satisfies these conditions is called a *metric*.

These properties of the Hamming distance, which are easy to establish, also ensure that it is a well-behaved measure of distance.

The error-correcting properties of a code are intimately connected with the Hamming distances that separate the codewords. Particularly important is the *smallest* Hamming distance between two codewords.

> ## Definition
>
> The **minimum distance** δ of a code is the smallest Hamming distance between two distinct codewords.

An (n, k) code with minimum distance δ is sometimes referred to as an (n, k, δ) **code**. For example, the minimum distance of the code

$$\{0000, 0011, 0101, 0110, 1001, 1010, 1100, 1111\}$$

is 2, and so this is a (4, 3, 2) code. Similarly, the minimum distance of the n-fold repetition code $R(n)$ is n, and so $R(n)$ is an $(n, 1, n)$ code.

Problem 1.8

Write down the minimum distance of each of the following codes:

(a) $\{000000, 001110, 010101, 011011, 100011, 101101, 110110, 111000\}$;

(b) $\{0000000, 0011101, 0101011, 0110110, 1000111, 1011010, 1101100, 1110001\}$.

Problem 1.9

(a) Explain why a code with minimum distance 3 can detect and correct up to one error.

(b) Explain why a code with minimum distance 4 can detect up to two errors and correct up to one error.

We now use the concept of Hamming distance to state a very important theorem, of which the results of Example 1.4 and Problem 1.9 are direct consequences.

> ## Theorem 1.1
>
> Let C be a code with minimum distance δ. If δ is odd, then C can detect and correct up to $(\delta - 1)/2$ errors.
>
> If δ is even, then C can detect up to $\delta/2$ errors and correct up to $(\delta - 2)/2$ errors.

Using $\lfloor x \rfloor$ to denote the integer part of x, we see that a code of minimum distance δ can correct $\lfloor (\delta - 1)/2 \rfloor$ errors.

Proof

Any decoding process operates by finding the codeword as close as possible to the word received — when a binary word $\mathbf{x}$ is received, the decoding process estimates that the unique codeword $\mathbf{c}$ that minimizes $d(\mathbf{x}, \mathbf{c})$ is the one most likely to have been transmitted, if such a codeword exists.

Suppose that t errors affect a transmitted codeword $\mathbf{c}$ — that is, a binary word $\mathbf{x}$ is received that satisfies $d(\mathbf{x}, \mathbf{c}) = t$. Let $\mathbf{y}$ be any codeword distinct from $\mathbf{c}$.

The definition of minimum distance ensures that $\delta \leq d(\mathbf{y}, \mathbf{c})$, and so, by the triangle property of the Hamming distance,

$$d(\mathbf{y}, \mathbf{c}) \leq d(\mathbf{y}, \mathbf{x}) + d(\mathbf{x}, \mathbf{c}).$$

So we have

$$\delta \leq d(\mathbf{y}, \mathbf{c}) \leq d(\mathbf{y}, \mathbf{x}) + d(\mathbf{x}, \mathbf{c}) = d(\mathbf{y}, \mathbf{x}) + t.$$

Thus

$$\delta - t \leq d(\mathbf{y}, \mathbf{x}), \text{ for any codeword } \mathbf{y} \text{ distinct from } \mathbf{c}.$$

This means that, if $t < \delta - t$, and so $t < \delta/2$, then **c** is the codeword that minimizes $d(\mathbf{x}, \mathbf{c})$ — in other words, the decoding process can find **c** from a knowledge of the received word **x**.

If δ is odd, then $t < \delta/2$ whenever $t \leq (\delta - 1)/2$;

if δ is even, then $t < \delta/2$ whenever $t \leq (\delta - 2)/2$.

Thus the code can *correct* up to $(\delta - 1)/2$ errors when δ is odd, and up to ~~$\delta/2$~~ $(\delta-2)/2$ errors when δ is even.

When δ is even and $t = \delta/2$, then it is possible for the received word **x** to be equidistant from two codewords — that is, there exists a codeword **y** distinct from the transmitted codeword **c** such that $d(\mathbf{x}, \mathbf{y}) = d(\mathbf{x}, \mathbf{c}) = t$. In this case, the decoding process can *detect* that t errors have occurred, but cannot determine which codeword was transmitted. ∎

Problem 1.10

Use Theorem 1.1 to answer the following questions:

(a) how many errors can be detected and corrected by a code of minimum distance 5?

(b) how many errors can be detected and corrected by each of the codes in Problem 1.8?

We saw in Example 1.4 that repetition codes are very inefficient. The final example in this section is of a single-error-correcting code with rate $1/2$ — a marked improvement on the repetition codes $R(2)$ and $R(3)$.

Example 1.5

Suppose that we wish to encode all binary words of length 3 in such a way that one error can be corrected. To do this, we add three check bits to each message, to yield a code of length 6. Each codeword **x** has six bits, so we can write **x** as $x_1 x_2 x_3 x_4 x_5 x_6$, where x_i denotes the ith bit of **x**. The bits x_1, x_2 and x_3 form the message, and we choose the check bits x_4, x_5 and x_6 so that the sums

$$x_2 + x_3 + x_4, \ x_1 + x_3 + x_5 \text{ and } x_1 + x_2 + x_6$$

are all even. We thus obtain the code

$$\{000000, 001110, 010101, 011011, 100011, 101101, 110110, 111000\}.$$

The messages are

000, 001, 010, 011,
100, 101, 110, 111.

To encode 010, for example, we adjoin the fourth bit 1, fifth bit 0 and sixth bit 1, and obtain 010101.

In order to decode a received word, we compare it with each codeword in turn. If the received word is a codeword, then we can safely assume that it is the codeword transmitted, and we simply read off the first three bits to obtain the message. If the received word is not a codeword, then we choose the codeword from which the received word has smallest Hamming distance. For example, if we receive 101011, then we may assume that 100011 was intended and that the third bit is wrong, so the message is 100. Similarly, if we receive 011000, we assume that 111000 was sent and that the first bit is wrong, so the message is 111.

This code is suitable for use on a channel for which we may assume that at most one error has affected any transmitted codeword. For, if at most one bit is corrupted in each transmitted codeword, then any word received is either a codeword, or lies at Hamming distance 1 from a codeword.

This decoding scheme works because the minimum distance of the code is 3. This means that, if a codeword is transmitted and only one bit is corrupted, then the received word differs from the intended codeword in only one place. However, it differs from *any other codeword* in at least two places. ∎

Decoding by comparison as in Example 1.5 is a system that works well, provided that the code is short and does not have many codewords. For many purposes, longer codes are necessary, and it is cheaper to use codes for which there are decoding algorithms. If a transmitted codeword can be affected by two or more errors, then we may be in trouble; for example, in the above example, if 010101 is transmitted and the third and fifth places are corrupted by noise, then the received word is 011111; in this case it is assumed that 011011 was transmitted, so the codeword is decoded as 011 instead of 010.

Note that the use of an unsuitable code — or a communication channel being affected by an atypical number of errors — can cause things to go disastrously wrong.

Problem 1.11 ————————————————————————

In each of the following cases, assume that the number of errors introduced is within the error-correcting capability of the code.

(a) Two codewords from the code of Example 1.5 are transmitted, but are affected by errors. The binary words received are 100110 and 011001. Which codewords were sent?

(b) Consider the code

{0000000, 1101001, 0101010, 1000011, 1001100, 0100101, 1100110, 0001111, 1110000, 0011001, 1011010, 0110011, 0111100, 1010101, 0010110, 1111111}.

Two codewords are transmitted, and the binary words received are 1110001 and 0111000. Which codewords were sent?

(c) Consider the code

{0000000000, 1001001110, 0110110001, 1111111111}.

Two codewords are transmitted, and the binary words received are 1101101110 and 1111110001. Which codewords were sent?

After reading this section, you should be able to:

- explain what are meant by the terms *communication channel*, *block code*, *encoding*, *decoding*, *systematic encoding rule*, *weight* and *Hamming distance*;

- appreciate the difference between *error detection* and *error correction*;

- define the *length*, *dimension*, *rate* and *minimum distance* of a code;

- explain what are meant by the terms *repetition code* and *even-weight code*.

- appreciate the connection between the minimum distance of a code and its error-detecting and error-correcting capabilities.

2 Linear codes

The main challenge of coding theory is to find good codes — that is, codes that transmit information at reasonable rates, yet are able to correct a suitable number of transmission errors. As we have seen in the previous section, simple repetition codes do not fulfil this criterion. In order to find more sophisticated methods of constructing codes, and to give us a language and notation to work with, we turn to linear algebra.

2.1 The definition of a linear code

Suppose that we have two binary words x and y, each of length n. Then $x = x_1 x_2 \ldots x_n$, where x_i denotes the ith bit of x, and similarly, $y = y_1 y_2 \ldots y_n$. We can obtain a third binary word $z = z_1 z_2 \ldots z_n$ by adding x and y together bit by bit, according to the rules

$$0 + 0 = 0, \quad 0 + 1 = 1, \quad 1 + 0 = 1, \quad 1 + 1 = 0.$$

In other words, $z = x + y$, where $z_i = x_i + y_i$ (modulo 2) for $i = 1, \ldots, n$.

For example,

$$00111 + 10101 = 10010 \quad \text{and} \quad 1011010 + 0010100 = 1001110.$$

Problem 2.1

In each of the following cases, add the binary words x and y:

(a) $x = 1011$ and $y = 0101$;

(b) $x = 1101$ and $y = 0000$;

(c) $x = 11101$ and $y = 11101$.

Problem 2.2

What answer is obtained when a binary word is added to itself?

Using the idea of modulo 2 addition, we can define the concept of a *linear code*. Most of the codes in this unit are linear codes.

Definition

A **linear code** is a code in which the sum (modulo 2) of any two codewords is also a codeword — that is, whenever x and y are codewords, then so is $x + y$.

For example, the code

$\{0000, 0101, 1010, 1111\}$

is a linear code, since the sum of any two of these codewords is a codeword. On the other hand, the code

$\{1001, 1010, 0011, 1111\}$

is not a linear code, since the sum of the last two codewords is not a codeword.

Note that, if x is any codeword in a linear code, then the code must also contain $x + x$, which is the zero word 0, by the result of Problem 2.2. Thus, any linear code must contain 0.

Problem 2.3

Is either of the following codes a linear code?

(a) {0000000, 0011101, 0101011, 0110110,
      1000111, 1011010, 1101100, 1110001};

(b) {0000000, 0010110, 0011001, 0100101,
      0101010, 1000011, 1001100, 1110000}.

Problem 2.4

Five of the eight codewords of a linear code are

> 0001111, 0110101, 1010011, 1011100, 1100110.

Find the other three codewords.

Another useful concept is the *weight* of a codeword.

Definition

The **weight** $w(\mathbf{x})$ of a binary word $\mathbf{x}$ is the number of 1s in $\mathbf{x}$.

For example, the weight of 10111011 is six, the weight of 000101010 is three, and the weight of 00000 is zero. Note that, if **0** is the zero word, then $w(\mathbf{x}) = d(\mathbf{x}, \mathbf{0})$, where d is the Hamming distance.

Theorem 2.1

For a linear code, the weight w possesses the following properties:

(a) for each pair of codewords $\mathbf{x}$ and $\mathbf{y}$,

$$d(\mathbf{x}, \mathbf{y}) = w(\mathbf{x} + \mathbf{y});$$

(b) the minimum distance is the smallest non-zero weight among the codewords.

Problem 2.5

Prove Theorem 2.1.

Problem 2.6

Prove that, for any two codewords $\mathbf{x}$ and $\mathbf{y}$,

(a) $w(\mathbf{x} + \mathbf{y}) \leq w(\mathbf{x}) + w(\mathbf{y})$;

(b) $w(\mathbf{x} + \mathbf{y}) \geq w(\mathbf{x}) - w(\mathbf{y})$.

2.2   Generator sets and matrices

Since the sum of any two codewords of a linear code is also a codeword, we must be able to find a minimal set of codewords with the property that every codeword can be obtained by adding codewords in this minimal set. Such a minimal set, which is not unique, is called a **generator set** for the code. If the code has dimension k, any generator set consists of k codewords, none of which can be formed by adding any of the others in the set.

For example, a generator set for the linear code

> {0000000, 0011101, 0101011, 0110110,
> 1000111, 1011010, 1101100, 1110001}

is   ⟨0011101, 0101011, 1000111⟩,

You met this code in Problem 2.3(a).

We use angled brackets for generator sets.

since the other five codewords can be obtained by adding these codewords; for example,

1101100 = 0101011 + 1000111.

Problem 2.7

Find another generator set for this code.

Problem 2.8

Find generator sets for the following linear codes:

(a) {0000, 0011, 0101, 0110, 1001, 1010, 1100, 1111};

(b) {000000, 001110, 010101, 011011, 100011, 101101, 110110, 111000}.

We can form the words in a generator set into a $k \times n$ matrix, as follows.

> ## Definition
>
> A $k \times n$ matrix **G** is a **generator matrix** for an (n, k) linear code C if the binary words that can be expressed as a sum of a subset of the rows of **G** are exactly the codewords of C.

A given code can have several different generator matrices.

Example 2.1

A generator set for the code

{000000, 001110, 010101, 011011, 100011, 101101, 110110, 111000}

You met this code in Problem 2.8(b).

is   ⟨100011, 010101, 001110⟩.

It follows that a generator matrix for this code is

$$\mathbf{G} = \begin{bmatrix} 1 & 0 & 0 & 0 & 1 & 1 \\ 0 & 1 & 0 & 1 & 0 & 1 \\ 0 & 0 & 1 & 1 & 1 & 0 \end{bmatrix}$$

Note that

each individual row of **G** is a codeword;

the sum of the first and second rows is the codeword 110110;

the sum of the first and third rows is the codeword 101101;

the sum of the second and third rows is the codeword 011011;

the sum of all three rows is the codeword 111000;

the sum of any row with itself is the codeword 000000.

We can therefore obtain all of the codewords by adding rows.   ∎

Problem 2.9

(a) Write down a generator matrix for the code in Problem 2.4.

(b) Write down a generator matrix for the code in Problem 2.8(a).

We shall use the generator matrix **G** to describe a simple way of encoding messages — that is, finding a simple rule for assigning a unique codeword to each possible message of k bits. We shall adopt matrix notation and write a binary word **m** as a row vector — that is, as a matrix with only one row.

Let a message **m** be a binary word of length k written as a row vector. The matrix product **mG** is a binary word of length n, which must be a codeword since **mG** is a sum of rows of **G**. If the bits $m_{j_1}, m_{j_2}, ..., m_{j_t}$ of **m** are 1 and all the other bits of **m** are 0, then **mG** can be obtained by adding rows $j_1, j_2, ...,$ j_t of **G**. It can be shown that 2^k different binary words of length n can be obtained by adding rows of **G**, and hence that no two distinct messages **m** of length k can give rise to the same codeword **mG**.

Example 2.2

Consider the (6, 3) code

{000000, 001110, 010101, 011011, 100011, 101101, 110110, 111000}.

This code has the 3×6 generator matrix

$$\mathbf{G} = \begin{bmatrix} 1 & 0 & 0 & 0 & 1 & 1 \\ 0 & 1 & 0 & 1 & 0 & 1 \\ 0 & 0 & 1 & 1 & 1 & 0 \end{bmatrix}$$

A message **m** of length 3 can be encoded by evaluating the matrix product **mG**. For example, if **m** = 110, then the codeword that corresponds to 110 is

$$\begin{bmatrix} 1 & 1 & 0 \end{bmatrix} \begin{bmatrix} 1 & 0 & 0 & 0 & 1 & 1 \\ 0 & 1 & 0 & 1 & 0 & 1 \\ 0 & 0 & 1 & 1 & 1 & 0 \end{bmatrix} = \begin{bmatrix} 1 & 1 & 0 & 1 & 1 & 0 \end{bmatrix}$$

Similarly, if **m** = 111, then the corresponding codeword is

$$\begin{bmatrix} 1 & 1 & 1 \end{bmatrix} \begin{bmatrix} 1 & 0 & 0 & 0 & 1 & 1 \\ 0 & 1 & 0 & 1 & 0 & 1 \\ 0 & 0 & 1 & 1 & 1 & 0 \end{bmatrix} = \begin{bmatrix} 1 & 1 & 1 & 0 & 0 & 0 \end{bmatrix}.$$

Note that this encoding rule is systematic — in the above example, the message appears as the first three bits of the corresponding codeword. This is because the first three columns of **G** in the example above are columns 1, 2 and 3 of the 3×3 identity matrix. ∎

When calculating the matrix product **mG** we carry out addition and multiplication modulo 2. We summarize the rules as follows:

+	0	1
0	0	1
1	1	0

×	0	1
0	0	0
1	0	1

The 3×3 identity matrix is the matrix

$$\begin{bmatrix} 1 & 0 & 0 \\ 0 & 1 & 0 \\ 0 & 0 & 1 \end{bmatrix}$$

Definition

A $k \times n$ generator matrix is in **standard form** when the first k columns form the $k \times k$ identity matrix $\mathbf{I}_k$.

An encoding rule which uses a $k \times n$ generator matrix **G** is systematic whenever k of the n columns of **G** are distinct columns of the $k \times k$ identity matrix $\mathbf{I}_k$. If columns **i** of $\mathbf{I}_k$ forms column j_i of **G**, then the ith bit of each message appears at the jth bit of the corresponding codeword.

Problem 2.10

The following matrix is a generator matrix for a (7, 4) code.

$$\mathbf{G} = \begin{bmatrix} 1 & 1 & 1 & 0 & 0 & 0 & 0 \\ 1 & 0 & 0 & 1 & 1 & 0 & 0 \\ 0 & 1 & 0 & 1 & 0 & 1 & 0 \\ 1 & 1 & 0 & 1 & 0 & 0 & 1 \end{bmatrix}$$

(a) Use the matrix **G** to encode the messages

(1) 1011; (2) 0001; (3) 1101; (4) 0000.

(b) Show that this encoding method is systematic. Which columns of **G** form the $k \times k$ identity matrix?

2.3   Parity check matrices

The method of adding two binary words of the same length provides us with a way of expressing the idea of noise on a communication channel.

Consider a codeword of length n, transmitted on a noisy channel and received with some bits in error. We can think of the resulting word received as being the sum (as defined above) of the transmitted codeword and an error word of length n:

(received word) = (transmitted codeword) + (error word).

The bits in the error word are 1 in exactly those places affected by noise in the codeword. All other bits in the error word are 0. For example, suppose that the transmitted codeword 10100 is received as 11100, with its second bit in error. We consider the codeword to have been affected by the error word 01000, since

11100 = 10100 + 01000.

Problem 2.11 ⎯⎯⎯⎯⎯⎯⎯⎯⎯⎯⎯⎯⎯⎯⎯⎯⎯⎯⎯⎯⎯⎯

(a)   The codeword 0001111 is affected by errors in the first and fourth bits. What is the error word, and which word is received?

(b)   The codeword 0001111 is transmitted again, and is affected by errors in the second, third and seventh bits. What is the error word, and which word is received?

We now turn to the problem of constructing codes. We again adopt matrix notation and write a codeword x as a row vector — that is, as a matrix with only one row. Then x^T, the *transpose* of x, is a column vector — a matrix with only one column.

For example, let x be a codeword with n bits, so that $x = x_1 x_2 \ldots x_n$. Then we can write

$$x = [x_1 x_2 \ldots x_n] \quad \text{and} \quad x^T = \begin{bmatrix} x_1 \\ x_2 \\ \vdots \\ x_n \end{bmatrix}$$

(a $1 \times n$ matrix)   (an $n \times 1$ matrix)

Linear codes have the following very useful property. To each (n, k) linear code there corresponds an $(n - k) \times n$ matrix H of 0s and 1s, with no row or column consisting entirely of 0s, and with the property that the code contains exactly those binary words x satisfying the matrix equation $Hx^T = 0^T$, where 0^T is the column vector consisting of $n - k$ zeros. We give this matrix H a special name.

Definition

Let C be an (n, k) linear code. A **parity check matrix** H is an $(n - k) \times n$ matrix with the property that the codewords of C are precisely the binary words x that satisfy the matrix equation $Hx^T = 0^T$.

A code can have several different parity check matrices.

For example, the linear code {0000, 0011, 1100, 1111} is a (4, 2) code and a parity check matrix for this code is the 2×4 matrix

$$H = \begin{bmatrix} 1 & 1 & 0 & 0 \\ 1 & 1 & 1 & 1 \end{bmatrix}$$

Note that the codewords are precisely the codewords $\mathbf{x} = x_1 x_2 x_3 x_4$ with the property $\mathbf{H}\mathbf{x}^T = \mathbf{0}^T$ — that is,

$$\begin{bmatrix} 1 & 1 & 0 & 0 \\ 1 & 1 & 1 & 1 \end{bmatrix} \begin{bmatrix} x_1 \\ x_2 \\ x_3 \\ x_4 \end{bmatrix} = \begin{bmatrix} 0 \\ 0 \end{bmatrix}$$

It follows that x_1, x_2, x_3 and x_4 satisfy the two equations

$$\begin{aligned} x_1 + x_2 \qquad\qquad &= 0 \ (\text{modulo } 2) \\ x_1 + x_2 + x_3 + x_4 &= 0 \ (\text{modulo } 2), \end{aligned}$$

and these equations lead to exactly the codewords listed above.

The reason for the name *parity check matrix* is that, for an (n, k) code, the matrix equation $\mathbf{H}\mathbf{x}^T = \mathbf{0}^T$ is a shorthand way of writing down a set of $n - k$ homogeneous simultaneous linear equations in the variables $x_1, x_2, \ldots, x_n$. If the jth row of $\mathbf{H}$ has entries of 1 in the columns $m_1, m_2, \ldots, m_j$, then the bit-sum $x_{m_1} + x_{m_2} + \ldots + x_{m_j}$ is 0 (modulo 2). In other words, a binary word $\mathbf{x}$ satisfies $\mathbf{H}\mathbf{x}^T = \mathbf{0}^T$ if and only if the sums (obtained by ordinary addition) of certain of its bits (determined by $\mathbf{H}$) are even — that is, they have even parity. The $n - k$ linear equations are therefore referred to as **parity check equations** of the code.

Example 2.3

The three-fold repetition code $R(3)$, introduced in Section 1, contains just two codewords, 000 and 111. These are the 3-bit binary words $\mathbf{x}$ that satisfy $x_1 = x_2 = x_3$, and so the parity check equations are

$$x_1 + x_2 = 0 \ (\text{modulo } 2), \quad x_2 + x_3 = 0 \ (\text{modulo } 2), \quad x_1 + x_3 = 0 \ (\text{modulo } 2).$$

Note that these three equations are not linearly independent: each equation is the sum of the other two.

Since $R(3)$ is a (3, 1) code, any parity check matrix must be a 2×3 matrix — that is, its rows must correspond to two of the three possible parity check equations. There are three different ways in which two of the equations can be chosen, and the resulting matrices are

$$\begin{bmatrix} 1 & 1 & 0 \\ 0 & 1 & 1 \end{bmatrix}, \quad \begin{bmatrix} 1 & 1 & 0 \\ 1 & 0 & 1 \end{bmatrix}, \quad \begin{bmatrix} 0 & 1 & 1 \\ 1 & 0 & 1 \end{bmatrix}.$$

However, these are not the only possible parity check matrices for $R(3)$. Since the order in which we write the parity check equations is unimportant, the order in which we write the rows of a parity check matrix is also unimportant, and so the following matrices are also parity check matrices for $R(3)$:

$$\begin{bmatrix} 0 & 1 & 1 \\ 1 & 1 & 0 \end{bmatrix}, \quad \begin{bmatrix} 1 & 0 & 1 \\ 1 & 1 & 0 \end{bmatrix}, \quad \begin{bmatrix} 1 & 0 & 1 \\ 0 & 1 & 1 \end{bmatrix}. \qquad\blacksquare$$

Example 2.4

Consider the code

$$\{000000, 001110, 010101, 011011, 100011, 101101, 110110, 111000\}.$$

A word $\mathbf{x}$ of length 6 is a codeword in this code if and only if the bit-sums $x_2 + x_3 + x_4$, $x_1 + x_3 + x_5$ and $x_1 + x_2 + x_6$ have even parity. The parity check equations are therefore

$$\begin{aligned} x_2 + x_3 + x_4 \qquad\qquad\quad &= 0 \ (\text{modulo } 2) \\ x_1 \qquad + x_3 \qquad + x_5 \qquad &= 0 \ (\text{modulo } 2) \\ x_1 + x_2 \qquad\qquad\quad + x_6 &= 0 \ (\text{modulo } 2). \end{aligned}$$

Writing these in matrix form, we obtain the matrix equation

$$\begin{bmatrix} 0 & 1 & 1 & 1 & 0 & 0 \\ 1 & 0 & 1 & 0 & 1 & 0 \\ 1 & 1 & 0 & 0 & 0 & 1 \end{bmatrix} \begin{bmatrix} x_1 \\ x_2 \\ x_3 \\ x_4 \\ x_5 \\ x_6 \end{bmatrix} = \begin{bmatrix} 0 \\ 0 \\ 0 \end{bmatrix}$$

Since $n = 6$ and $k = 3$, the above 3×6 matrix **H** is a parity check matrix for this code. ∎

Definition

An $(n - k) \times n$ parity check matrix is in **standard form** when the last $(n - k)$ columns form the $(n - k) \times (n - k)$ identity matrix $\mathbf{I}_{n - k}$.

Problem 2.12

Find a parity check matrix for each of the following codes:

(a) the even-weight code {0000, 0101, 1010, 1111};

(b) the four-fold repetition code $R(4)$.

Problem 2.13

Describe the codes with the following parity check matrices — you need not write the codes out in full:

(a) $\mathbf{H} = \begin{bmatrix} 1 & 1 & 1 & 1 & 1 & 1 \end{bmatrix}$; (b) $\mathbf{H} = \begin{bmatrix} 1 & 1 & 0 & 0 & 0 \\ 1 & 0 & 1 & 0 & 0 \\ 1 & 0 & 0 & 1 & 0 \\ 1 & 0 & 0 & 0 & 1 \end{bmatrix}$

We now show how the parity check matrix of a code can be the key to fast decoding. Suppose that a codeword **x** from a code with parity check matrix **H** is transmitted over a communication channel. Let **e** denote the error word that affects **x**, so that the word $\mathbf{r} = \mathbf{x} + \mathbf{e}$ is received. Then

$$\mathbf{Hr}^T = \mathbf{H}(\mathbf{x} + \mathbf{e})^T = \mathbf{H}(\mathbf{x}^T + \mathbf{e}^T) = \mathbf{Hx}^T + \mathbf{He}^T = \mathbf{0}^T + \mathbf{He}^T = \mathbf{He}^T.$$

Since **x** is a codeword, $\mathbf{Hx}^T = \mathbf{0}^T$.

In other words, the column vector of length $n - k$ that results from pre-multiplying the transpose of the received word by the parity check matrix is independent of the codeword transmitted. It depends only on the errors that have occurred. It is, in fact, the sum of those columns of **H** that correspond to the corrupted bits. This column vector of length $n - k$ is called the *syndrome* of the errors.

Definition

For an (n, k) code with parity check matrix **H**, the **error syndrome** of a received word **r** is the column vector $\mathbf{Hr}^T$ of length $n - k$.

Example 2.5

Consider the code

{000000, 001110, 010101, 011011, 100011, 101101, 110110, 111000}.

Suppose that a codeword is transmitted, and that the word 101111 is received. Using the parity check matrix **H** obtained in Example 2.4, we find that

$$\mathbf{H}\begin{bmatrix}1 & 0 & 1 & 1 & 1 & 1\end{bmatrix}^T = \begin{bmatrix} 0 & 1 & 1 & 1 & 0 & 0 \\ 1 & 0 & 1 & 0 & 1 & 0 \\ 1 & 1 & 0 & 0 & 0 & 1 \end{bmatrix}\begin{bmatrix} 1 \\ 0 \\ 1 \\ 1 \\ 1 \\ 1 \end{bmatrix} = \begin{bmatrix} 0 \\ 1 \\ 0 \end{bmatrix}$$

Thus the column vector $[0\ 1\ 0]^T$ is the syndrome of the errors that have affected the transmitted codeword. This vector is the 5th column of $\mathbf{H}$, so we suspect that the codeword 101101 was sent, and that x_5 was corrupted. ∎

Problem 2.14

A code has parity check matrix

$$\mathbf{H} = \begin{bmatrix} 1 & 0 & 0 & 0 & 0 & 0 & 1 & 0 & 0 & 0 \\ 1 & 1 & 0 & 0 & 0 & 0 & 0 & 1 & 0 & 0 \\ 1 & 1 & 0 & 0 & 0 & 1 & 0 & 0 & 1 & 0 \\ 0 & 1 & 0 & 0 & 0 & 0 & 0 & 0 & 0 & 1 \\ 0 & 0 & 1 & 0 & 0 & 1 & 0 & 0 & 0 & 0 \\ 1 & 0 & 0 & 1 & 0 & 1 & 0 & 0 & 0 & 0 \\ 0 & 1 & 0 & 0 & 1 & 1 & 0 & 0 & 0 & 0 \end{bmatrix}$$

After transmission over a noisy channel, the word $\mathbf{r}$ = 0101100011 was received. Which codeword is most likely to have been transmitted?

In order to be able to base a decoding method on syndromes as illustrated above, we must show that the syndrome calculated from a received word uniquely identifies the error word most likely to have occurred. Let $\mathbf{H}$ be the parity check matrix of an (n, k, δ) linear code, and suppose that $\mathbf{e}_1$ and $\mathbf{e}_2$ are two distinct non-zero error words of length n and weight at most $(\delta - 1)/2$ if δ is odd, and $(\delta - 2)/2$ if δ is even. We can now show that $\mathbf{e}_1$ and $\mathbf{e}_2$ have different syndromes. For, if $\mathbf{He}_1^T = \mathbf{He}_2^T$, then

$$\mathbf{H}(\mathbf{e}_1 + \mathbf{e}_2)^T = \mathbf{H}(\mathbf{e}_1^T + \mathbf{e}_2^T) = \mathbf{He}_1^T + \mathbf{He}_2^T = \mathbf{0}^T.$$

This implies that $\mathbf{e}_1 + \mathbf{e}_2$ is a codeword.

Now recall from Problem 2.6(a) that, for any pair of codewords $\mathbf{x}$ and $\mathbf{y}$ in a linear code, the weight function w satisfies the inequality

$$w(\mathbf{x} + \mathbf{y}) \leq w(\mathbf{x}) + w(\mathbf{y}).$$

Using the above definition of $\mathbf{e}_1$ and $\mathbf{e}_2$, we obtain

$$w(\mathbf{e}_1 + \mathbf{e}_2) \leq w(\mathbf{e}_1) + w(\mathbf{e}_2) \leq 2[(\delta - 1)/2] < \delta.$$

It follows from Problem 2.5(b) that $\mathbf{e}_1 + \mathbf{e}_2$ cannot be a codeword. This contradiction leads us to conclude that different error vectors of weight at most $[(\delta - 1)/2]$ give rise to different error syndromes.

2.4 The Hamming codes

R. W. Hamming (1915 – 1998)

The Hamming codes are an easily-constructed family of single-error correcting codes that can be decoded using error syndromes. We now construct the shortest non-trivial code in this family, the (7, 4) Hamming code. This was one of the earliest codes to become widely known — details were published by R. W. Hamming in 1950.

We have seen that the syndrome of a received word that is in error in the ith bit is exactly the ith column of the parity check matrix of the code in

The shortest (trivial) Hamming code is the three-fold repetition code $R(3)$.

Hamming's paper is reproduced in the Appendix at the end of the unit.

21

use. Thus the parity check matrix of a single-error correcting code must have distinct columns, none of them consisting only of zeros.

Consider an (n, k) code that corrects a single error, and let $m = n - k$. Then a parity check matrix of this code has $2^m - 1$ possible columns. If $m = 3$, then there are seven possible columns. Thus, a single-error correcting code with three parity checks has length at most 7. If we form a matrix $\mathbf{H}$ from all seven columns, writing the columns in increasing binary order, we obtain the matrix

$$\mathbf{H} = \begin{bmatrix} 0 & 0 & 0 & 1 & 1 & 1 & 1 \\ 0 & 1 & 1 & 0 & 0 & 1 & 1 \\ 1 & 0 & 1 & 0 & 1 & 0 & 1 \end{bmatrix}$$

This matrix is the parity check matrix of a $(7, 4)$ code with $2^4 = 16$ codewords — namely:

{0000000, 1101001, 0101010, 1000011,
1001100, 0100101, 1100110, 0001111,
1110000, 0011001, 1011010, 0110011,
0111100, 1010101, 0010110, 1111111}.

This code has a simple decoding algorithm. If a transmitted codeword is received with its ith bit in error, then the syndrome calculated from the received word is the ith column of $\mathbf{H}$. We have arranged things so that, reading from top to bottom, the ith column of $\mathbf{H}$ is the binary representation of the number i. We can therefore immediately correct the bit that is in error.

For example, suppose that the word $\mathbf{r} = 1110010$ is received. Then the error syndrome is

$$\mathbf{Hr}^T = \begin{bmatrix} 0 & 0 & 0 & 1 & 1 & 1 & 1 \\ 0 & 1 & 1 & 0 & 0 & 1 & 1 \\ 1 & 0 & 1 & 0 & 1 & 0 & 1 \end{bmatrix} \begin{bmatrix} 1 \\ 1 \\ 1 \\ 0 \\ 0 \\ 1 \\ 0 \end{bmatrix} = \begin{bmatrix} 1 \\ 1 \\ 0 \end{bmatrix}$$

This gives the sixth column of $\mathbf{H}$, which is the binary representation of the number 6. Thus the sixth bit is in error, and the codeword transmitted was 1110000.

Problem 2.15

(a) Use the parity check matrix to decode the following received words:

(1) 1001010; (2) 1110001; (3) 0111000.

(b) Compare your answers to parts (a)(2) and (a)(3) with the results obtained in Problem 1.11(b).

It is possible to construct a Hamming code of length $2^m - 1$ for each integer m, where $m \geq 2$. A parity check matrix has m rows and $2^m - 1$ columns. It follows that the code has $2^m - 1 - m$ message bits. All Hamming codes have minimum distance 3, and so each is a $(2^m - 1, 2^m - 1 - m, 3)$ code, for some integer m.

Problem 2.16

Write down the parity check matrix for the Hamming code of length 15. What is the rate of this code?

2.5 Perfect codes

Let **c** be a codeword in a linear (n, k, δ) code; then each codeword has n bits.

There is exactly one binary word at Hamming distance 0 from **c** — namely, **c** itself.

There are exactly $\binom{n}{1}$ different ways of changing one bit of **c**, and so there are $\binom{n}{1}$ binary words at Hamming distance 1 from **c**.

Similarly, there are $\binom{n}{i}$ binary words at Hamming distance i from **c**.

The number of ways of choosing i bits from n is

$$\binom{n}{i} = \frac{n!}{i!(n-i)!}.$$

Suppose that t is an integer such that $t \le (\delta - 1)/2$ if δ is odd, and $t \le (\delta - 2)/2$ if δ is even. Then, by Theorem 1.1, no binary word can lie within Hamming distance t of two distinct codewords. Altogether there are 2^k codewords, and there are

$$1 + \binom{n}{1} + \binom{n}{2} + \ldots + \binom{n}{t}$$

binary words within Hamming distance t of each. Thus, there are at least

$$2^k \left(1 + \binom{n}{1} + \binom{n}{2} + \ldots + \binom{n}{t} \right)$$

n-bit binary words. However, the total number of n-bit binary words is 2^n, and so

$$1 + \binom{n}{1} + \binom{n}{2} + \ldots + \binom{n}{t} \le 2^{n-k}.$$

This inequality is called the **Hamming inequality** and the upper bound given by this inequality is the **Hamming bound**.

Problem 2.17 ─────────────────────────

Use the Hamming inequality to determine whether there is a linear code with parameters

(a) $n = 21, k = 14, \delta = 5$;

(b) $n = 64, k = 51, \delta = 5$;

(c) $n = 64, k = 51, \delta = 7$.

The Hamming inequality is used to define a particular type of linear code, as follows.

Definition

A **perfect code** is a linear error-correcting code for which the Hamming bound is attained.

Note that every Hamming code is a perfect code, since if $n = 2^m - 1$, then we have

$$1 + \binom{n}{1} = 2^m = 2^{n-k},$$

and so the Hamming bound is attained.

Problem 2.18

Which of the following codes is perfect?

(a) the code

{000000, 001110, 010101, 011011, 100011, 101101, 110110, 111000};

(b) the four-fold repetition code $R(4)$;

(c) the five-fold repetition code $R(5)$.

The result of Problem 2.18, parts (b) and (c), can be generalized to show that the n-fold repetition code $R(n)$ is perfect whenever n is an odd number. Any n-bit binary word must have a majority of its bits the same, and so is decodable.

Perfect codes are codes of length n that have the property that *every* binary word of length n has a unique 'nearest neighbour' codeword. If a binary word can be found that has two or more 'nearest neighbour' codewords, then the code is not perfect. For example, no codeword of the non-perfect code in Problem 2.18(a) is at Hamming distance 1 from 100100, but there are three codewords at Hamming distance 2 — namely, 000000, 101101 and 110110.

If an (n, k) code is perfect, then *every* word of length n can be decoded. This is not necessarily 'perfect' in practice — if more errors affect a codeword than the code is designed to correct, then it may be preferable for decoding to be impossible, rather than to yield an incorrect estimate of the message being transmitted.

2.6 Computer activities

The computer activities for this section are described in the *Computer Activities Booklet*.

> After reading this section, you should be familiar with the rules for adding binary words, and be able to:
>
> - explain what are meant by the terms *error word*, *parity check matrix* and *linear code*;
>
> - encode messages by using the *generator matrix* of a linear code;
>
> - decode a linear code by using its parity check matrix to calculate the error syndrome of the received binary word;
>
> - construct a Hamming code of length $2^m - 1$, for any integer $m \geq 2$;
>
> - test whether or not a given code is perfect.

3 New codes from old

In this section we describe some methods for obtaining a new code from a given one. First, we explain what we mean by *equivalent codes*.

3.1 Equivalent codes

Suppose that we take a linear code and rearrange the bits in each codeword according to some fixed rule; then we obtain a new code with the same length, dimension and minimum distance as the original code. If we similarly rearrange the columns of the parity check matrix of the original code, then we obtain a parity check matrix for the new code.

Example 3.1

The (7, 4) Hamming code is given below on the left. The codewords of code C on the right are obtained by rewriting each codeword $\mathbf{x} = x_1\,x_2\,x_3\,x_4\,x_5\,x_6\,x_7$ of the Hamming code as $\mathbf{y} = x_5\,x_6\,x_7\,x_3\,x_4\,x_2\,x_1$.

Hamming code		*code C*	
0000000	1111111	0000000	1111111
1101001	0010110	0010111	1101000
0101010	1010101	0100110	1011001
1000011	0111100	0110001	1001110
1001100	0110011	1000101	0111010
0100101	1011010	1010010	0101101
1100110	0011001	1100011	0011100
0001111	1110000	1110100	0001011

For example,
$$\mathbf{x} = 1101001$$
in the Hamming code becomes
$$\mathbf{y} = 0010111$$
in code C.

A parity check matrix for the Hamming code is

$$
\begin{array}{ccccccc}
1 & 2 & 3 & 4 & 5 & 6 & 7
\end{array}
$$
$$
\begin{bmatrix}
0 & 0 & 0 & 1 & 1 & 1 & 1 \\
0 & 1 & 1 & 0 & 0 & 1 & 1 \\
1 & 0 & 1 & 0 & 1 & 0 & 1
\end{bmatrix}
$$

Rearranging the columns appropriately, we obtain a parity check matrix for code C:

$$
\begin{array}{ccccccc}
5 & 6 & 7 & 3 & 4 & 2 & 1
\end{array}
$$
$$
\begin{bmatrix}
1 & 1 & 1 & 0 & 1 & 0 & 0 \\
0 & 1 & 1 & 1 & 0 & 1 & 0 \\
1 & 0 & 1 & 1 & 0 & 0 & 1
\end{bmatrix}
$$
∎

This idea leads to the following definition.

Definition

Two codes are **equivalent** if the codewords of one can be obtained by rearranging the bits of each codeword of the other according to some fixed rule.

Example 3.1 illustrates the following result.

Theorem 3.1

Any $(2^m - 1, 2^m - 1 - m, 3)$ linear code is equivalent to the Hamming code of the same length and dimension.

For this reason, *any $(2^m - 1, 2^m - 1 - m, 3)$ linear code is known as a Hamming code*.

Proof

A parity check matrix $\mathbf{H}$ for a $(2^m - 1, 2^m - 1 - m, 3)$ code has m rows and $2^m - 1$ columns. Since $\delta = 3$, one error can be corrected, so no two error words of weight 1 give rise to the same syndrome — that is, no two columns of $\mathbf{H}$ are the same. Thus, all possible non-zero columns of length m appear exactly once in $\mathbf{H}$. This means that the columns of $\mathbf{H}$ can be rearranged to give a parity check matrix for the $(2^m - 1, 2^m - 1 - m)$ Hamming code. In other words, the given code is equivalent to the Hamming code with the same length and dimension. ∎

Problem 3.1

(a) Consider the following codes:

code *A*: {0000, 0101, 1010, 1111};

code *B*: {0000, 1100, 0011, 1111}.

How can the bits of each codeword of code *A* be rearranged to form the codewords of code *B*?

(b) Find a parity check matrix for code *B* by using a parity check matrix for code *A* found in Problem 2.12(a).

Example 3.1 continued

The parity check matrix of the (7, 4) Hamming code, with the columns arranged in increasing binary order, is

$$\begin{bmatrix} 0 & 0 & 0 & 1 & 1 & 1 & 1 \\ 0 & 1 & 1 & 0 & 0 & 1 & 1 \\ 1 & 0 & 1 & 0 & 1 & 0 & 1 \end{bmatrix}$$

Rearranging the columns so that we obtain a partitioned matrix with the identity matrix at the end, we obtain

$$\mathbf{H} = \begin{bmatrix} 1 & 1 & 1 & 0 & | & 1 & 0 & 0 \\ 0 & 1 & 1 & 1 & | & 0 & 1 & 0 \\ 1 & 0 & 1 & 1 & | & 0 & 0 & 1 \end{bmatrix}$$

$$\quad\quad\uparrow \quad\quad\quad\quad \uparrow$$
$$\quad\quad \mathbf{A} \quad\quad\quad\quad \mathbf{I}$$

This is not the only standard parity check matrix for a (7, 4) Hamming code. The order of the columns of **A** does not matter — any order is acceptable.

To obtain an equivalent code with a parity check matrix in this form, it is sufficient to re-order each codeword so that the first 4 bits are the message bits. ∎

This leads to the following theorem.

Theorem 3.2

Every (n, k) linear code is equivalent to a code with a systematic encoding rule — that is, a code whose parity check matrix can be written in the standard form

$$\mathbf{H} = [\mathbf{A} \,|\, \mathbf{I}],$$

where **A** is an $(n - k) \times k$ matrix of 0s and 1s, and **I** is the $(n - k) \times (n - k)$ identity matrix.

To find an equivalent code with a parity check matrix in this standard form, it is sufficient to re-order each codeword of a given code so that the first k bits are the message bits.

A code is normally equivalent to more than one other code with a parity check matrix in this form.

In circumstances where we do not need to distinguish between equivalent codes, it is helpful to use a parity check matrix in standard form. However, sometimes one code is much easier to decode than another equivalent code. For instance, the neat decoding algorithm of the (7, 4) Hamming code, described in Section 2, is an immediate consequence of the ordering of the columns (in binary order) in the parity check matrix. The standard matrix **H** is the parity check matrix of the Hamming code above.

We conclude this subsection with a simple result that yields parity check matrices from generator matrices, and *vice versa*. We shall see that, if **H** is a parity check matrix and **G** is a generator matrix for a given code, then $\mathbf{H}\mathbf{G}^T = \mathbf{0}$. This leads to the following result.

If a parity check matrix **H** of a code *C* is expressed in standard form $\mathbf{H} = [\mathbf{A} \,|\, \mathbf{I}]$, then the matrix $\mathbf{G} = [\mathbf{I} \,|\, \mathbf{A}^T]$ is a generator matrix for *C*.

Example 3.1 continued

A parity check matrix of the (7, 4) Hamming code is

$$H = \begin{array}{c} \begin{array}{ccccccc} 1 & 2 & 3 & 4 & 5 & 6 & 7 \end{array} \\ \begin{bmatrix} 0 & 0 & 0 & 1 & 1 & 1 & 1 \\ 0 & 1 & 1 & 0 & 0 & 1 & 1 \\ 1 & 0 & 1 & 0 & 1 & 0 & 1 \end{bmatrix} \end{array}$$

We can put it into standard form by rearranging the columns as follows:

$$\begin{array}{c} \begin{array}{cccccc} 3 & 5 & 6 & 7 & 4 & 2 & 1 \end{array} \\ \begin{bmatrix} 0 & 1 & 1 & 1 & 1 & 0 & 0 \\ 1 & 0 & 1 & 1 & 0 & 1 & 0 \\ 1 & 1 & 0 & 1 & 0 & 0 & 1 \end{bmatrix} \end{array}$$

By the above remarks, a generator matrix in standard form is

$$\begin{array}{c} \begin{array}{cccccc} 3 & 5 & 6 & 7 & 4 & 2 & 1 \end{array} \\ \begin{bmatrix} 1 & 0 & 0 & 0 & 0 & 1 & 1 \\ 0 & 1 & 0 & 0 & 1 & 0 & 1 \\ 0 & 0 & 1 & 0 & 1 & 1 & 0 \\ 0 & 0 & 0 & 1 & 1 & 1 & 1 \end{bmatrix} \end{array}$$

Rearranging the columns in their original order, we obtain the generator matrix

$$G = \begin{array}{c} \begin{array}{ccccccc} 1 & 2 & 3 & 4 & 5 & 6 & 7 \end{array} \\ \begin{bmatrix} 1 & 1 & 1 & 0 & 0 & 0 & 0 \\ 1 & 0 & 0 & 1 & 1 & 0 & 0 \\ 0 & 1 & 0 & 1 & 0 & 1 & 0 \\ 1 & 1 & 0 & 1 & 0 & 0 & 1 \end{bmatrix} \end{array}$$

∎

Problem 3.2

Use the above method to find a parity check matrix for the code
    {0000000, 0011101, 0101011, 0110110,
    1000111, 1011010, 1101100, 1110001}.

Hint A generator set for this code is given at the beginning of Section 2.2.

3.2   Cyclic codes

Sometimes when we rearrange the bits of each codeword in a given code according to a particular fixed rule, we find that the equivalent code obtained is not a new code, but is the same as the original code.

Example 3.2

Consider the following code C:
    {0000, 0011, 0101, 0110, 1001, 1010, 1100, 1111}.

Let us find a new code equivalent to C by 'cycling' the first bit of each codeword to the end; that is, whenever

$$c = x_1 x_2 x_3 x_4$$

is a codeword of C, we make

$$c' = x_2 x_3 x_4 x_1$$

a codeword in the new code. We thus obtain the code
    {0000, 0110, 1010, 1100, 0011, 0101, 1001, 1111}.

This is just the code C with the codewords listed in a different order.   ∎

This motivates the following definition.

Definition

A **cyclic code** is a code of length n with the property that, whenever

$\mathbf{x} = x_1 x_2 \ldots x_n$ is a codeword, then so also is $\mathbf{x}' = x_2 \ldots x_n x_1$.

Problem 3.3 ———————————————————

Which of the following codes is cyclic?

(a) {0 0 0 0, 0 1 0 1, 1 0 1 0, 1 1 1 1};

(b) {0 0 0 0, 1 1 0 0, 0 0 1 1, 1 1 1 1}.

Cyclic codes have been much studied by mathematicians, since they are particularly amenable to algebraic treatment. They are consequently the most important type of block code found in practical use, since the mathematics needed for encoding and decoding can be conveniently performed by modern digital circuits.

For each positive integer m, there is a cyclic Hamming code of length $2^m - 1$. In other words, each Hamming code is equivalent to a cyclic Hamming code.

Problem 3.4 ———————————————————

The word 1001110 is a codeword of the (7, 4) cyclic Hamming code. Find six other codewords and a parity check matrix.

3.3 Dual codes

We have encountered the idea of duality several times in this course. For example, in *Design 1* we formed the dual of an incidence structure by interchanging the roles of *points* and *lines* and re-interpreting 'contains' as 'occurs in' and *vice versa*. In this subsection, we explore the consequences of interchanging the roles of the *rows of a parity check matrix* and the code words of a given linear code.

Example 3.6

A parity check matrix in standard form for the (7, 4) Hamming code is

$$\mathbf{H} = \begin{bmatrix} 1 & 1 & 1 & 0 & 1 & 0 & 0 \\ 0 & 1 & 1 & 1 & 0 & 1 & 0 \\ 1 & 0 & 1 & 1 & 0 & 0 & 1 \end{bmatrix}$$

There are $2^{7-4} = 8$ possible sums of rows of $\mathbf{H}$:

binary word	rows of H included in the sum
0000000	no rows (or any row added to itself)
1110100	row 1
0111010	row 2
1011001	row 3
1001110	rows 1 and 2
0101101	rows 1 and 3
1100011	rows 2 and 3
0010111	rows 1, 2 and 3

The eight binary words obtained by adding rows of the matrix $\mathbf{H}$ form a (7, 3) *simplex code*. ∎

See Section 1 of *Design 1* for the definitions of *simplex* and *n-cube*.

Note that the binary word obtained by adding rows 1 and 3 can also be found by calculating the matrix product

$$\begin{bmatrix} 1 & 0 & 1 \end{bmatrix}\begin{bmatrix} 1 & 1 & 1 & 0 & 1 & 0 & 0 \\ 0 & 1 & 1 & 1 & 0 & 1 & 0 \\ 1 & 0 & 1 & 1 & 0 & 0 & 1 \end{bmatrix} = \begin{bmatrix} 0 & 1 & 0 & 1 & 1 & 0 & 1 \end{bmatrix}$$

and that the binary word obtained by adding rows 1, 2 and 3 can be found by calculating the matrix product

$$\begin{bmatrix} 1 & 1 & 1 \end{bmatrix}\begin{bmatrix} 1 & 1 & 1 & 0 & 1 & 0 & 0 \\ 0 & 1 & 1 & 1 & 0 & 1 & 0 \\ 1 & 0 & 1 & 1 & 0 & 0 & 1 \end{bmatrix} = \begin{bmatrix} 0 & 0 & 1 & 0 & 1 & 1 & 1 \end{bmatrix}$$

An (n, k) linear code C is defined by a parity check matrix $\mathbf{H}$. Each row of $\mathbf{H}$ is a parity check on the codewords — that is, we have $\mathbf{h}\mathbf{x}^T = \mathbf{0}$ for each row $\mathbf{h}$ of $\mathbf{H}$, if and only if the binary word $\mathbf{x}$ is a codeword.

Now the identity $\mathbf{h}\mathbf{x}^T = \mathbf{0}$ is symmetrical in $\mathbf{h}$ and $\mathbf{x}$ — that is, $\mathbf{h}\mathbf{x}^T = \mathbf{0}$ if and only if $\mathbf{x}\mathbf{h}^T = \mathbf{0}$.

> Here $\mathbf{0}$ is the 1 x 1 matrix [0]. The transpose of a matrix product is obtained by the rule $(\mathbf{AB})^T = \mathbf{B}^T\mathbf{A}^T$; it follows that $(\mathbf{h}\mathbf{x}^T)^T = \mathbf{x}^{TT}\mathbf{h}^T = \mathbf{x}\mathbf{h}^T$.

What happens if we think of each row of a parity-check matrix $\mathbf{H}$ as a codeword $\mathbf{x}$ of a new code? Is there a linear code of length n that contains the rows of $\mathbf{H}$ among its codewords? Such a code would necessarily contain all the sums of rows of $\mathbf{H}$, since the sum of any two codewords in a linear code is a codeword. Since $\mathbf{H}$ has $n - k$ rows, there are 2^{n-k} possible subsets of rows of $\mathbf{H}$.

In general, the binary word obtained by adding rows 1, 2, ..., k of $\mathbf{H}$ is given by the matrix product $\mathbf{m}\mathbf{H}$, where $\mathbf{m}$ is the row vector of length $n - k$ with entries 1 in places 1, 2, ..., k and 0 elsewhere. If $\mathbf{H}$ is written in standard form,

$$\mathbf{H} = [\mathbf{A} \mid \mathbf{I}],$$

we have

$$\mathbf{m}\mathbf{H} = [\mathbf{m}\mathbf{A} \mid \mathbf{m}\mathbf{I}] = [\mathbf{m}\mathbf{A} \mid \mathbf{m}],$$

so different choices of $\mathbf{m}$ yield different codewords.

We have shown that the sum of each possible subset of rows of $\mathbf{H}$ is a unique binary word. In other words, exactly 2^{n-k} different words of length n can be obtained from the rows of $\mathbf{H}$. These words are therefore the codewords of an $(n, n - k)$ code, called the **dual code** C^* of the original code C. The message bits of C^* are the last $n - k$ bits of each codeword. Even if the parity check matrix $\mathbf{H}$ of the original code C is not in standard form, we can still obtain the $(n, n - k)$ dual code C^* by calculating all sums of subsets of rows of $\mathbf{H}$.

> The following diagram illustrates the $(3, 2, 2)$ simplex code — the dual of the $(3, 1, 3)$ Hamming code $R3$.

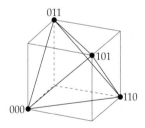

In general, a **simplex code** is the dual of a Hamming code: the dual of a $(2^m - 1, 2^m - 1 - m, 3)$ Hamming code is a $(2^m - 1, m, 2^{m-1})$ simplex code. The simplex code of length $2^m - 1$ contains the zero word and $2^m - 1$ words of weight 2^{m-1}. If the codewords are considered as vertices of the n-cube, then they form a *regular n-simplex* — that is, a simplex with edges of the same length.

> The choice of parity check matrix for C does not affect the resulting dual code. This is because any two parity check matrices for C are row-equivalent.

Note that the parity check matrix of a code C is a generator matrix for the dual code C^*. We use this fact to give a formal definition of a *dual code*.

Definition

Let $\mathbf{H}$ be a parity check matrix of an (n, k) linear code C. The **dual** of C is the $(n, n - k)$ linear code C^* with generator matrix $\mathbf{H}$.

We can now prove that the dual of a dual code is the original code.

Theorem 3.3: duality theorem

Let C be a linear code. Then $(C^*)^* = C$.

Proof

Let $\mathbf{H}$ be the parity check matrix of the linear code C, and let $\mathbf{G}$ be the parity check matrix of the dual code C^*. A binary word $\mathbf{h}$ of length n is thus a codeword of C^* precisely when $\mathbf{Gh}^T = \mathbf{0}$.

Since each row of $\mathbf{H}$ is a codeword of C^*, it follows that $\mathbf{GH}^T = \mathbf{0}$.

Taking transposes, we obtain the matrix equation $\mathbf{HG}^T = \mathbf{0}$. In other words, each row $\mathbf{g}$ of $\mathbf{G}$ satisfies the equation $\mathbf{Hg}^T = \mathbf{0}$.

$(\mathbf{GH}^T)^T = (\mathbf{H}^T)^T \mathbf{G}^T = \mathbf{HG}^T$.

This implies that each row of $\mathbf{G}$ is a codeword in C. But $\mathbf{G}$ is the parity check matrix of C^*. It follows from the above discussion that every codeword in $(C^*)^*$ is also a codeword in C. However, the definition of the dual of a code ensures that the dimension of $(C^*)^*$ is $n-(n-k) = k$. Thus $(C^*)^*$ contains as many codewords as C. We conclude that $(C^*)^* = C$. ∎

Corollary

Let C be a linear code. Then the parity check matrix of the dual code C^* is a generator matrix for C.

Example 3.7

The following code C contains all the even-weight words of length 4:

{0000, 0011, 0101, 0110, 1001, 1010, 1100, 1111}.

It follows from a result analogous to that of Problem 2.13(a) that the parity check matrix is $\mathbf{H} = [1\ 1\ 1\ 1]$. There are exactly two binary words that can be expressed as a sum of rows of $\mathbf{H}$ — namely, 0000 and 1111. These two words form the dual of the code C. Thus, *the dual of the even-weight code of length 4 is the four-fold repetition code R(4)*.

The result of Problem 2.12(b) establishes that a parity check matrix of the four-fold repetition code $R(4)$ is

$$\begin{bmatrix} 1 & 1 & 0 & 0 \\ 1 & 0 & 1 & 0 \\ 1 & 0 & 0 & 1 \end{bmatrix}$$

The eight binary words that can be expressed as sums of rows of this matrix are exactly the codewords of C. This illustrates the Corollary to Theorem 3.3, that *the parity check matrix of the dual is a generator matrix for the original code*.

The arguments in this example can easily be generalized to show that the dual of the n-fold repetition code $R(n)$ is the even-weight code of length n. ∎

Problem 3.5 ——————————————————————

Let C be the code {0000, 0101, 1010, 1111}.

Use the parity check matrix

$$\mathbf{H} = \begin{bmatrix} 1 & 0 & 1 & 0 \\ 0 & 1 & 0 & 1 \end{bmatrix}$$

This parity check matrix was found in Problem 2.12(a).

to find the codewords of the dual code C^*. What do you notice about your result?

——

In Example 3.7 and Problem 3.5, we obtained the dual codes of two cyclic codes. In each case, the dual code is also cyclic. We now prove that these are special cases of a general result.

> **Theorem 3.4**
>
> The dual of a cyclic code is cyclic.

Proof

Let C be a cyclic code of length n, and let $\mathbf{h} = h_1 h_2 \ldots h_n$ be a row of a parity check matrix $\mathbf{H}$. Then the codewords of C^* are precisely the parity checks of C.

Let $\mathbf{c} = c_1 c_2 \ldots c_n$ be a codeword of C. Then $\mathbf{h}\mathbf{c}^T = 0$, and

$$\mathbf{h}^*\mathbf{c}^T = [h_2 \ldots h_n h_1] \begin{bmatrix} c_1 \\ \vdots \\ c_{n-1} \\ c_n \end{bmatrix}$$

$$= [h_2 c_1 + \ldots + h_n c_{n-1} + h_1 c_n]$$

$$= [h_1 c_n + h_2 c_1 + h_3 c_2 + \ldots + h_{n-1} c_{n-2} + h_n c_{n-1}]$$

$$= [h_1 h_2 h_3 \ldots h_n] \begin{bmatrix} c_n \\ c_1 \\ c_2 \\ \vdots \\ c_{n-1} \end{bmatrix}$$

$$= \mathbf{h}\mathbf{d}^T,$$

where $\mathbf{d} = c_n c_1 c_2 \ldots c_{n-1}$. It follows that $\mathbf{h}^*\mathbf{c}^T = 0$, and so $\mathbf{h}^*$ is a parity check of C. Thus $\mathbf{h}^*$ is a codeword of the dual code C^*. It follows that C^* is cyclic. ∎

3.4 Extended codes

An easy way to obtain a new code is to *extend* a given (n, k, δ) code by adding an overall parity check. We do this by adding an extra bit to each codeword in such a way that the resulting binary word of length $n + 1$ has even weight, so we add a 0 to each codeword of even weight, and a 1 to each codeword of odd weight. The length of the extended code is $n + 1$, but as the number of codewords is unchanged, the dimension is still k. Since each codeword in the extended code has even weight, and the minimum distance of a code is the smallest non-zero weight amongst its codewords, it follows that the minimum distance of the extended code is

$\delta + 1$ if δ is odd,

δ if δ is even.

Problem 3.6 ─────────────────────────────────

How many errors can the extended code detect and correct in each of the following cases?

(a) the original code has minimum distance 6;

(b) the original code has minimum distance 7.

───

Example 3.8

Consider the (6,3) code

{000000, 001110, 010101, 011011, 100011, 101101, 110110, 111000}.

We can extend this code to obtain a (7, 3) code C with the following codewords:

parity check		parity check	
000000	0	100011	1
001110	1	101101	0
010101	1	110110	0
011011	0	111000	1

This code C is the $(7, 3)$ simplex code, the dual of the $(7, 4)$ Hamming code. ∎

We met a simplex code equivalent to this one earlier in the section.

Just as all Hamming codes with the same length and dimension are equivalent, so their duals (the simplex codes) are equivalent.

It is easy to construct a parity check matrix for the code obtained by extending an (n, k) code with parity check matrix **H**. The addition of an overall parity check is equivalent to adding a row of 1s to **H**. Since the extended code has length $n + 1$, its parity check matrix is

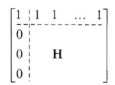

Here we have added the overall parity check as the *first* bit of each codeword, for reasons that will become apparent in Section 4.

Example 3.10

The following matrix is a parity check matrix for the $(8, 4, 4)$ code obtained by extending a $(7, 4)$ Hamming code. This $(8, 4, 4)$ code is self-dual.

$$\mathbf{H} = \begin{bmatrix} 1 & 1 & 1 & 1 & 1 & 1 & 1 & 1 \\ 0 & 0 & 0 & 0 & 1 & 1 & 1 & 1 \\ 0 & 0 & 1 & 1 & 0 & 0 & 1 & 1 \\ 0 & 1 & 0 & 1 & 0 & 1 & 0 & 1 \end{bmatrix}$$

∎

3.5 The [a | a + b] construction

So far in this section we have introduced various ways in which a new code can be obtained from a given one. We now describe how two codes of the same length n can be combined to form a new code of length $2n$. The resulting codes have good error-correcting properties. We introduce the construction by an example.

Example 3.11

Consider the following two codes of length 4:

    Code A   {0000, 0011, 0101, 0110, 1001, 1010, 1100, 1111}

    Code B   {0000, 1111}

In the new code, the first four bits of each codeword form a codeword **a** of Code A, and the last four bits are obtained by adding to this codeword a codeword **b** of Code B. Since Code B has just two codewords, 0000 and 1111, each codeword of Code A yields two new eight-bit codewords of the form **a** | **a** + **b**. For example, the codeword **a** = 1001 of code A yields the two new codewords

    1001 | 1001 + 0000 — that is, 1001 | 1001

and

    1001 | 1001 + 1111 — that is, 1001 | 0110.

This construction gives the following sixteen new codewords of length 8:

a	a + 0000	a	a + 1111
0000	0000	0000	1111
0011	0011	0011	1100
0101	0101	0101	1010
0110	0110	0110	1001
1001	1001	1001	0110
1010	1010	1010	0101
1100	1100	1100	0011
1111	1111	1111	0000

In fact, this 'new' code is one that you have already met. It is the $(8, 4, 4)$ extended Hamming code described in Example 3.10. ∎

The above example shows how two codes of length 4, one with eight codewords and the other with two, can be 'put together' to give a new code of length 8 with sixteen codewords. We generalize this method in the following theorem.

Theorem 3.5

Let A be an (n, k_A, δ_A) code and B be an (n, k_B, δ_B) code, and let δ be the smaller of $2\delta_A$ and δ_B. Then the code C whose codewords are all the binary words of the form $[a \mid a + b]$, where a is a codeword of code A and b is a codeword of code B, is a $(2n, k_A + k_B, \delta)$ code.

Proof

Since code A contains 2^{k_A} codewords and code B contains 2^{k_B} codewords, it follows that code C must contain $2^{k_A + k_B}$ codewords. Thus the dimension of code C is $k_A + k_B$.

In order to show that the minimum distance of code C is δ, the smaller of $2\delta_A$ and δ_B, we let a and b be codewords of minimum weight in codes A and B, respectively. But $[a \mid a] = [a \mid a + 0]$ is a codeword of code C with weight $2\delta_A$, and $[0 \mid b] = [0 \mid 0 + b]$ is a codeword of code C with weight δ_B, so the minimum non-zero weight of the codewords in code C cannot exceed the smaller of these — that is, δ.

We now let a_1 and a_2 be codewords of code A and b_1 and b_2 be codewords of code B. Then the Hamming distance between the codewords $[a_1 \mid a_1 + b_1]$ and $[a_2 \mid a_2 + b_2]$ of code C is equal to

$$w(a_1 + a_2) + w(a_1 + a_2 + b_1 + b_2). \qquad (*)$$

If b_1 and b_2 are distinct codewords, it follows from Problem 2.6(b) that

$$w(a_1 + a_2 + b_1 + b_2) \geq w(b_1 + b_2) - w(a_1 + a_2),$$

and hence

$$d([a_1 \mid a_1 + b_1], [a_2 \mid a_2 + b_2]) \geq w(b_1 + b_2) = d(b_1, b_2) \geq \delta_B.$$

If $b_1 = b_2$, then $b_1 + b_2 = 0$, and so, by (*)

$$d([a_1 \mid a_1 + b_1], [a_2 \mid a_2 + b_2]) = 2w(a_1 + a_2) = 2\delta_A.$$

It follows that the distance between any two codewords in code C is at least δ. This shows that δ is the minimum distance of code C. ∎

Problem 3.7

In Example 3.11 we applied the above construction to two codes, A and B. List the codewords of the code obtained by this construction when these two codes are interchanged. Which code detects more errors?

Let A be an (n, k_A) code with generator matrix $\mathbf{G}_A$, and let B be an (n, k_B) code with generator matrix $\mathbf{G}_B$.

(a) Find a generator matrix for the code C obtained from the codes A and B by the $[\mathbf{a} \mid \mathbf{a} + \mathbf{b}]$ construction.

(b) Let $\mathbf{H}_A$ be a parity check matrix for code A and $\mathbf{H}_B$ be a parity check matrix for code B. Show that

$$\mathbf{H} = \begin{bmatrix} \mathbf{H}_A & \mathbf{0} \\ \mathbf{H}_B & \mathbf{H}_B \end{bmatrix}$$

is a parity check matrix for code C.

3.6 Computer activities

The computer activities for this section are described in the *Computer Activities Booklet*.

After working through this section, you should be able to:

- understand the terms equivalent codes, cyclic code and dual code;

- appreciate that every linear code is equivalent to a linear code whose parity check matrix is in standard form;

- describe the connection between parity check matrices and generator matrices in standard form;

- extend a code by adding an *overall parity check*;

- describe the $[\mathbf{a} \mid \mathbf{a} + \mathbf{b}]$ construction for obtaining a new code from two given codes of the same length.

4 First-order Reed-Muller codes

In this section we consider an important class of codes, introduced in the 1950s by I. S. Reed and D. E. Muller. One of these codes was used by the Mariner 9 space probe to Mars to send television pictures back to Earth.

4.1 Three special codes

This Hamming code is a member of a famous family of codes known as the *Reed-Muller codes*. Before we proceed to a definition of these codes, we look at this example from a different viewpoint.

We begin by looking at three examples.

Example 4.1: $\mathcal{R}(1)$

Consider the following code for which $n = k = 2$, and $\delta = 1$:

$\{00, 01, 10, 11\}$.

A generator matrix for this code is

$$\mathbf{G} = \begin{matrix} & \begin{matrix} 0 & 1 \end{matrix} \\ \begin{matrix} 1 \\ v_1 \end{matrix} & \begin{bmatrix} 1 & 1 \\ 0 & 1 \end{bmatrix} \end{matrix}$$

I. S. Reed (1923 –)

D. E. Muller (1924 –)

We have labelled the two columns of $\mathbf{G}$ with the two binary numbers 0 and 1 with one digit, and we have labelled the rows 1 and v_1. The four codewords can be written as sums of the rows, as follows:

0:	00
v_1:	01
1:	11
$1 + v_1$:	10

$\mathcal{R}(1)$

length $n = 2$;

dimension $k = 2$;

minimum distance $\delta = 1$;

■ number of codewords = 4.

Example 4.2: $\mathcal{R}(2)$

Consider the even-weight code of length 4 for which $n = 4$, $k = 3$ and $\delta = 2$:

$$\{0000, 0011, 0101, 0110, 1001, 1010, 1100, 1111\}.$$

A generator matrix for this code is:

$$\begin{array}{c} \begin{array}{cccc} 00 & 01 & 10 & 11 \end{array} \\ \mathbf{G} = \begin{array}{c} 1 \\ v_1 \\ v_2 \end{array} \begin{bmatrix} 1 & 1 & 1 & 1 \\ 0 & 0 & 1 & 1 \\ 0 & 1 & 0 & 1 \end{bmatrix} \end{array}$$

We have labelled the four columns of $\mathbf{G}$ from left to right with the 2-bit binary numbers, and we have labelled the rows 1, v_1 and v_2. The eight codewords can be written as sums of the rows, as follows:

0:	0000
v_1:	0011
v_2:	0101
$v_1 + v_2$:	0110
1:	1111
$1 + v_1$:	1100
$1 + v_2$:	1010
$1 + v_1 + v_2$:	1001

$\mathcal{R}(2)$

length $n = 4$

dimension $k = 3$;

minimum distance $\delta = 2$;

■ number of codewords = 8

Example 4.3: $\mathcal{R}(3)$ — the (8, 4, 4) extended Hamming code

In Example 3.10 we extended the (7, 4) Hamming code and obtained an (8, 4, 4) code with parity check matrix

$$\mathbf{H} = \begin{bmatrix} 1 & 1 & 1 & 1 & 1 & 1 & 1 & 1 \\ 0 & 0 & 0 & 0 & 1 & 1 & 1 & 1 \\ 0 & 0 & 1 & 1 & 0 & 0 & 1 & 1 \\ 0 & 1 & 0 & 1 & 0 & 1 & 0 & 1 \end{bmatrix} = \mathbf{G}$$

The (8, 4, 4) extended Hamming code is self-dual, so this parity check matrix $\mathbf{H}$ is also a generator matrix $\mathbf{G}$ for the code.

Below we have labelled the eight (2^3) columns of $\mathbf{G}$ from left to right with the 3-bit binary numbers 000 to 111, and we have labelled the rows 1, v_1, v_2 and v_3:

$$\begin{array}{c} \begin{array}{cccccccc} 000 & 001 & 010 & 011 & 100 & 101 & 110 & 111 \end{array} \\ \mathbf{G} = \begin{array}{c} 1 \\ v_1 \\ v_2 \\ v_3 \end{array} \begin{bmatrix} 1 & 1 & 1 & 1 & 1 & 1 & 1 & 1 \\ 0 & 0 & 0 & 0 & 1 & 1 & 1 & 1 \\ 0 & 0 & 1 & 1 & 0 & 0 & 1 & 1 \\ 0 & 1 & 0 & 1 & 0 & 1 & 0 & 1 \end{bmatrix} \end{array}$$

Note that, if we know the row and column numbers of an element of the matrix $\mathbf{G}$, then we can deduce the value of that element. For, each element in the first row is a 1. In the second row, the element in the jth column is equal to the left-most bit of the binary expansion of j. In the third row, the element in the jth column is equal to the middle bit of the binary expansion of j. In the fourth row, the element in the jth column is equal to the right-most bit of the binary expansion of j.

In other words, if the binary expansion of j is $v_1 v_2 v_3$, then the entry in row 1 of column j is 1, in row 2 of column j is v_1, in row 3 of column j is v_2, and in row 4 of column j is v_3.

If we add together two rows of $\mathbf{G}$, then we can easily obtain the resulting codeword. For example, the jth bit of the codeword obtained by adding the rows of $\mathbf{G}$ corresponding to v_1 and v_2 is equal to the sum (modulo 2) of the left-most and middle bits of the binary expansion of j:

	000	001	010	011	100	101	110	111
v_1	0	0	0	0	1	1	1	1
v_2	0	0	1	1	0	0	1	1
$v_1 + v_2$	0	0	1	1	1	1	0	0

We now have a new description for each codeword:

0	0000 0000
v_1	0000 1111
v_2	0011 0011
v_3	0101 0101
$v_2 + v_3$	0110 0110
$v_1 + v_3$	0101 1010
$v_1 + v_2$	0011 1100
$v_1 + v_2 + v_3$	0110 1001
1	1111 1111
$1 + v_1$	1111 0000
$1 + v_2$	1100 1100
$1 + v_3$	1010 1010
$1 + v_2 + v_3$	1001 1001
$1 + v_1 + v_3$	1010 0101
$1 + v_1 + v_2$	1100 0011
$1 + v_1 + v_2 + v_3$	1001 0110

$\mathcal{R}(3)$

length $n = 8$;

dimension $k = 4$;

minimum distance $\delta = 4$;

number of codewords = 16.

Conversely, each of the sixteen different linear combinations of 1, v_1, v_2 and v_3 corresponds to a codeword. We can think of each codeword as a linear function of three 'variables' v_1, v_2 and v_3. The jth bit of each codeword is equal to the value of the corresponding linear function when the values of v_1, v_2 and v_3 are chosen so that $v_1 v_2 v_3$ is the binary expansion of the integer j. ∎

4.2 The definition of a Reed-Muller code

The three codes considered above are members of an important family of codes known as the *first-order Reed-Muller codes*. We now formally define these codes. First, we introduce the ideas of a *Boolean variable* and a *Boolean function*.

Definition

A **Boolean variable** is a variable that can take only two values, usually 0 and 1. A **Boolean function** is a function of Boolean variables, which can itself take only the same two values.

We now describe the codes introduced in Section 4.1 in terms of Boolean algebra. For the code $\mathcal{R}(2)$, the eight codewords listed above correspond to the eight Boolean functions that are polynomials of degree at most 1 in the two Boolean variables v_1 and v_2. Similarly, for the code $\mathcal{R}(3)$, the sixteen codewords listed above correspond to the sixteen Boolean functions that are polynomials of degree at most 1 in the three Boolean variables v_1, v_2 and v_3. This leads to a general definition of the first-order Reed-Muller codes.

Definition

The set of binary words that correspond to all the Boolean functions of degree at most 1 in m variables, $v_1, v_2, ..., v_m$, is called the **first-order Reed-Muller code of length 2^m**, denoted by $\mathcal{R}(m)$.

Similarly, we can construct rth-order Reed-Muller codes, for any $r \geq 1$, by considering Boolean functions of degree at most r.

The order in which the values of each Boolean function are listed is irrelevant, as long as it is the same for each codeword. There are therefore many equivalent Reed-Muller codes of each possible length.

The first-order Reed-Muller codes $\mathcal{R}(1)$, $\mathcal{R}(2)$ and $\mathcal{R}(3)$ were discussed above.

What is the dimension of $\mathcal{R}(m)$?

It is easy to see that

the dimension of $\mathcal{R}(m)$ is $m + 1$,

as we can generalize from our analysis of $\mathcal{R}(3)$ to deduce that $\mathcal{R}(m)$ possesses a generator matrix whose rows correspond to the $m + 1$ Boolean functions $1, v_1, v_2, ..., v_m$.

What is the minimum distance of $\mathcal{R}(m)$?

In the case of $\mathcal{R}(3)$, there is one codeword of weight 0, there are fourteen codewords of weight 4, and there is one of weight 8, and so the minimum distance of the code is 4. A similar statement can be made about any first-order Reed-Muller code, since it follows from the properties of Boolean functions that $\mathcal{R}(m)$ has:

one codeword of weight 0,

$2^{m+1} - 2$ codewords of weight 2^{m-1},

one codeword of weight 2^m.

Since the minimum distance of a linear code is equal to the smallest weight of a non-zero codeword, the minimum distance of $\mathcal{R}(m)$ is 2^{m-1}.

It follows from the above discussion that

$\mathcal{R}(m)$ is a $(2^m, m + 1, 2^{m-1})$ code.

Problem 4.1

What is the rate of $\mathcal{R}(m)$? What happens to this rate as m increases?

We next show how a Reed-Muller code is built up from a Reed-Muller code of shorter length. To obtain the Reed-Muller code $\mathcal{R}(m + 1)$, we apply the $[\mathbf{a} \mid \mathbf{a} + \mathbf{b}]$ construction to the Reed-Muller code $\mathcal{R}(m)$ and the 2^m-fold repetition code $R(2^m)$. We explain why this works shortly. Before doing so, we look at two particular cases.

At the end of Section 3 we illustrated the [a|a + b] construction, taking code A to be the even-weight code of length 4, and code B to be the four-fold repetition code $R(4)$, and we obtained the (8, 4, 4) Hamming code. In other words, we obtained the Reed-Muller code $\mathcal{R}(3)$ by using the [a|a + b] construction with $A = \mathcal{R}(2)$ and $B = R(4)$.

We now repeat the process; we use the [a|a + b] construction taking A to be the code $\mathcal{R}(3)$ and B to be the eight-fold repetition code $R(8)$. It follows from Theorem 3.5 that we obtain a (16, 5, 4) code, and it is straightforward to verify that this code is indeed $\mathcal{R}(4)$.

Problem 4.2 ───────────────────────────────────────

We have seen that the 4×8 matrix

$$G_A = \begin{bmatrix} 1 & 1 & 1 & 1 & 1 & 1 & 1 & 1 \\ 0 & 0 & 0 & 0 & 1 & 1 & 1 & 1 \\ 0 & 0 & 1 & 1 & 0 & 0 & 1 & 1 \\ 0 & 1 & 0 & 1 & 0 & 1 & 0 & 1 \end{bmatrix}$$

is a generator matrix for $\mathcal{R}(3)$, and we know that

$$\mathbf{G}_B = [1\ 1\ 1\ 1\ 1\ 1\ 1\ 1]$$

is a generator matrix for $R(8)$.

Let $\mathbf{G}$ be the 5×16 matrix

$$\mathbf{G} = \begin{bmatrix} \mathbf{G}_A & \mathbf{G}_A \\ \mathbf{0} & \mathbf{G}_B \end{bmatrix}$$

Show that $\mathbf{G}$ is a generator matrix for $\mathcal{R}(4)$, and that, if we label the columns of $\mathbf{G}$ from left to right with the 4-bit binary numbers 0000 to 1111, then the rows of $\mathbf{G}$, labelled from top to bottom, correspond to the Boolean functions $1, v_1, v_2, v_3, v_4$ in four variables, as follows:

row 1 corresponds to 1;

row 2 corresponds to v_2;

row 3 corresponds to v_3;

row 4 corresponds to v_4;

row 5 corresponds to v_1.

───

We now state the main result of this section.

Theorem 4.1

The code $\mathcal{R}(m + 1)$ consists of all binary words of the form [a|a + b], where $\mathbf{a}$ is a codeword in $\mathcal{R}(m)$ and $\mathbf{b}$ is a codeword in the repetition code $R(2^m)$.

Proof

We have already seen that the 1×2^m matrix $\mathbf{G}_B = [1\ 1\ ...\ 1]$ is a generator matrix for the repetition code $R(2^m)$. Let $\mathbf{G}_A$ be a generator matrix for $\mathcal{R}(m)$, whose rows, labelled from top to bottom, correspond to the Boolean functions $1, v_1, v_2, ..., v_m$ in m variables.

Consider the code whose generator matrix is the $(m + 2) \times 2^{m+1}$ matrix

$$\mathbf{G} = \begin{bmatrix} \mathbf{G}_A & \mathbf{G}_A \\ 0...0 & 1...1 \end{bmatrix}$$

This code contains all words of the form [a|a], where $\mathbf{a}$ is a codeword in $\mathcal{R}(m)$. It also contains all words of the form [0|b], where $\mathbf{b}$ is a codeword in

$R(2^m)$. Since the new code is linear, it therefore contains all words of the form

$$[\mathbf{a}\,|\,\mathbf{a}] + [\mathbf{0}\,|\,\mathbf{b}] = [\mathbf{a}\,|\,\mathbf{a} + \mathbf{b}],$$

where $\mathbf{a}$ is in $\mathcal{R}(m)$ and $\mathbf{b}$ is in $R(2^m)$. In other words, $\mathbf{G}$ is a generator matrix for the code obtained by applying the $[\mathbf{a}\,|\,\mathbf{a} + \mathbf{b}]$ construction to $\mathcal{R}(m)$ and $R(2^m)$. Let us label the columns of $\mathbf{G}$ from left to right with the $(m + 1)$-bit binary numbers from $00 \ldots 0$ to $11 \ldots 1$. We can now regard each row of $\mathbf{G}$ as a Boolean function in $m + 1$ variables:

> row 1 corresponds to 1;
>
> row 2 corresponds to v_2;
>
> $\ldots$
>
> row m corresponds to v_m;
>
> row $m + 1$ corresponds to v_{m+1};
>
> row $m + 2$ corresponds to v_1.

In other words, $\mathbf{G}$ is a generator matrix for $\mathcal{R}(m + 1)$. ∎

First-order Reed-Muller codes can be decoded in several ways. One simple method, using a form of majority logic, is described below.

Problem 4.3

The following matrix $\mathbf{G}$ is a generator matrix for $\mathcal{R}(3)$:

$$\mathbf{G} = \begin{bmatrix} 1 & 1 & 1 & 1 & 1 & 1 & 1 & 1 \\ 0 & 0 & 0 & 0 & 1 & 1 & 1 & 1 \\ 0 & 0 & 1 & 1 & 0 & 0 & 1 & 1 \\ 0 & 1 & 0 & 1 & 0 & 1 & 0 & 1 \end{bmatrix}$$

(a) Use $\mathbf{G}$ to encode the following messages:

(1) 1101;   (2) 0110;   (3) 1000.

(b) Is this encoding rule for $\mathcal{R}(3)$ systematic?

The method of decoding by majority logic is best described by an example.

Example 4.1

Suppose that we transmit the codeword of $\mathcal{R}(3)$ that corresponds to the message $\mathbf{a} = a_1\, a_2\, a_3\, a_4$ encoded using the generator matrix

$$\mathbf{G} = \begin{bmatrix} 1 & 1 & 1 & 1 & 1 & 1 & 1 & 1 \\ 0 & 0 & 0 & 0 & 1 & 1 & 1 & 1 \\ 0 & 0 & 1 & 1 & 0 & 0 & 1 & 1 \\ 0 & 1 & 0 & 1 & 0 & 1 & 0 & 1 \end{bmatrix}$$

Let $\mathbf{r} = r_1\, r_2\, r_3\, r_4\, r_5\, r_6\, r_7\, r_8$ be the word received.

If we assume that no error has occurred in transmission, then $\mathbf{r} = \mathbf{a}\mathbf{G}$. This implies the following relationships between the bits of $\mathbf{r}$ and $\mathbf{a}$:

$$
\begin{aligned}
r_1 &= a_1 \\
r_2 &= a_1 & & & & + a_4 \\
r_3 &= a_1 & & + a_3 \\
r_4 &= a_1 & & + a_3 & & + a_4 \\
r_5 &= a_1 & + a_2 \\
r_6 &= a_1 & + a_2 & & & + a_4 \\
r_7 &= a_1 & + a_2 & + a_3 \\
r_8 &= a_1 & + a_2 & + a_3 & & + a_4.
\end{aligned}
$$

Remember that arithmetic is performed modulo 2.

We can express the last three bits of $\mathbf{a}$ in terms of the bits of $\mathbf{r}$ as follows:

$$a_2 = r_1 + r_5 \quad = r_2 + r_6 \quad = r_3 + r_7 \quad = r_4 + r_8$$
$$a_3 = r_1 + r_3 \quad = r_2 + r_4 \quad = r_5 + r_7 \quad = r_6 + r_8$$
$$a_4 = r_1 + r_2 \quad = r_3 + r_4 \quad = r_5 + r_6 \quad = r_7 + r_8.$$

There are thus four 'votes' each, for the values of a_2, a_3 and a_4. If one bit of r is corrupted in transmission, then the correct values of a_2, a_3 and a_4 are still obtained by a majority of three out of four votes in each case. The value of a_1 can then be found by majority logic, since

$$a_1 = r_1 \quad = r_2 + a_4 \quad = r_3 + a_3 \quad = r_5 + a_2.$$

If two bits of **r** are wrongly received, then this decoding algorithm fails, because there is a tie in the vote for the values of at least two of the bits of **a**. Thus $\mathcal{R}(3)$ can detect two errors and correct one error. Since $\mathcal{R}(3)$ has minimum distance 4, this is in accordance with Theorem 1.1. ∎

Problem 4.4

Decode each of the following received words, using the decoding algorithm just described for $\mathcal{R}(3)$:

(a) 11010101; (b) 00110110; (c) 10110110.

If possible, state which bits are in error in each received word.

There is another decoding method, which is unusual since it does not depend on modulo 2 arithmetic. It can be used when such codes are used on a *Gaussian channel*, which you can think of as a channel on which any real number can be transmitted; the received signal can then be decoded immediately, without transforming the received signal into 0s and 1s. A binary word is transmitted by sending a positive signal of predetermined value for a 0, and a negative signal of inverse value for a 1. A signal affected by noise is not necessarily inverted. Many communication channels can be satisfactorily modelled in this way. In particular, radio signals in space are transmitted on a noisy Gaussian channel. Most binary codes would be almost useless in such circumstances, whereas first-order Reed–Muller codes perform well when equipped with the decoding method described above.

4.3 The Golay codes

Let A denote the first-order Reed–Muller code of length 8 with generator matrix

$$\begin{bmatrix} 1 & 1 & 1 & 1 & 1 & 1 & 1 & 1 \\ 0 & 1 & 0 & 0 & 0 & 1 & 1 & 1 \\ 1 & 0 & 1 & 0 & 0 & 0 & 1 & 1 \\ 1 & 1 & 0 & 1 & 0 & 0 & 0 & 1 \end{bmatrix}$$

If we take the first-order Reed–Muller code $\mathcal{R}(3)$, introduced in this section, and rearrange the bits in each codeword in the order $x_4\, x_6\, x_3\, x_2\, x_1\, x_5\, x_7\, x_8$, then we obtain the codewords of code A. Thus code A is equivalent to $\mathcal{R}(3)$.

If we reverse the order of the first seven bits of each codeword of code A, we obtain the codewords of an equivalent first-order Reed–Muller code of length 8. Let us call this second code B. We can use codes A and B to construct an interesting pair of codes that have fascinated mathematicians since details were first published by M. J. E. Golay in 1949. This construction of the extended Golay code is based on an idea similar to the [**a** | **a** + **b**] construction described in Section 3.

M. J. E. Golay (1902 – 1989)

40

Definition

The **extended Golay code** *G(24)* is the code whose codewords are all the binary words that can be written in the form

$$[\mathbf{a}_1 + \mathbf{b} \mid \mathbf{a}_2 + \mathbf{b} \mid \mathbf{a}_1 + \mathbf{a}_2 + \mathbf{b}],$$

where $\mathbf{a}_1$ and $\mathbf{a}_2$ are codewords in A, and $\mathbf{b}$ is a codeword in B.

It follows from the definition that each codeword in the extended Golay code can be written as the sum of the binary words

$$[\mathbf{a}_1 \mid \mathbf{0} \mid \mathbf{a}_1], \; [\mathbf{0} \mid \mathbf{a}_2 \mid \mathbf{a}_2], \; [\mathbf{b} \mid \mathbf{b} \mid \mathbf{b}],$$

where $\mathbf{a}_1$ and $\mathbf{a}_2$ are codewords in A, and $\mathbf{b}$ is a codeword in B. Since there are 2^4 choices for each of $\mathbf{a}_1$, $\mathbf{a}_2$ and $\mathbf{b}$, the extended Golay code contains 2^{12} codewords.

The minimum distance of the extended Golay code is 8.

Thus $G(24)$ is a (24, 12, 8) code.

Let $\mathbf{G}_A$ and $\mathbf{G}_B$ be generator matrices of codes A and B, respectively. Then the 12×24 matrix

$$\mathbf{G} = \begin{bmatrix} \mathbf{G}_A & \mathbf{0} & \mathbf{G}_A \\ \mathbf{0} & \mathbf{G}_A & \mathbf{G}_A \\ \mathbf{G}_B & \mathbf{G}_B & \mathbf{G}_B \end{bmatrix}$$

is a generator matrix of $G(24)$.

Since the code $\mathcal{R}(3)$ of length 8 is self-dual, the matrix products $\mathbf{G}_A \mathbf{G}_A{}^T$ and $\mathbf{G}_B \mathbf{G}_B{}^T$ are both zero matrices. Consequently, $\mathbf{G}\mathbf{G}^T = 0$ — that is, $G(24)$ is also self-dual.

We can show that $\mathbf{G}$ is a generator matrix by extending the method used in the solution to Problem 3.8(a).

If we delete the last bit of each codeword of $G(24)$, we obtain a new code with length 23 and minimum distance 7.

Definition

The **Golay code** *G(23)* is the (23, 12, 7) code obtained from $G(24)$ by deleting the last bit of each codeword.

The extended Golay code $G(24)$ is therefore obtained by extending $G(23)$ in the manner described in Section 3.4.

Problem 4.5 —————————————————————————————

(a) What is the rate of $G(23)$?

(b) How many errors can $G(23)$ correct?

(c) Show that $G(23)$ is a perfect code.

You have now met all the perfect binary codes — namely, the repetition codes R(n), for all odd values of n, the Hamming codes, and the binary Golay code G(23).

It can be shown that the Golay codes are unique, in the sense that any (24, 12, 8) code is equivalent to G(24), and any (23, 12, 7) code is equivalent to G(23). Professor J. H. van Lint, whom you meet in the television programme for this unit, has described the existence of the Golay codes as a 'minor miracle'. Unfortunately, the mathematics required to study them in depth is beyond the scope of this unit.

4.4 The Mariner 9 code

In 1971, the Mariner 9 spacecraft transmitted a series of remarkable television pictures of the planet Mars back to Earth over a distance of 84 million miles. There had been previous missions to Mars, but none had sent back such accurate detail of the planet's surface. The achievement is all the more remarkable when we realize that the transmitter on board Mariner 9 had a power of only twenty watts; this should be compared with the Crystal Palace transmitter, which has a power of *forty thousand* watts and yet covers a range of less than sixty miles!

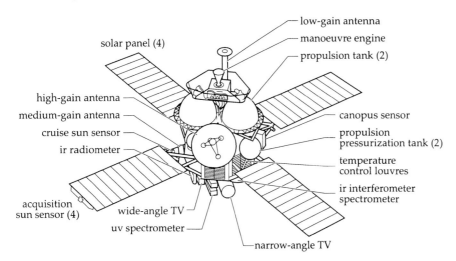

The feeble signal of Mariner 9 was all but lost in the radio noise of space, so much so that one would scarcely expect to receive any pictures at all. How, then, were such near-perfect pictures obtained?

The transmission techniques used by Mariner 9 were based on error-correcting codes, and it is these codes that we consider. Each picture transmitted by Mariner 9 is made up of over half a million tiny picture elements forming a rectangular array. Each element of the array is a uniform shade of grey, the precise shade being specified by a 9-bit binary number such as 110011010. The electronic sensing devices on board the spacecraft were extremely sensitive and could distinguish 512 levels of brightness, from black to white. An ordinary photograph shows no more than 10 shades of grey, but the extra information provided by Mariner 9 allowed parts of the grey scale to be expanded by special processing so as to bring out fine detail that would otherwise be invisible.

The $5\frac{1}{4}$ million bits representing a single picture were transmitted serially to Earth, and there translated back into tiny picture elements from which the picture could be reconstructed. But many bits were lost because of the incessant background noise from space and thermal noise from the electronics in the receiver.

The low power of the Mariner 9 transmitter made it very difficult to pick out its signal against the background noise, when the spacecraft was such a vast distance away from Earth. To distinguish 1s from 0s, one had to rely upon the received signal being above or below some threshold level. Noise causes us to confuse the two, and such errors are inevitable. The only answer was to have some means of correcting the errors after they had occurred; for this purpose Mariner 9 employed an error-correcting code in its transmission of the signal.

Instead of $5\frac{1}{4}$ million bits, Mariner 9 actually transmitted more than five times that number. The message was divided up into packets of six bits, and each was encoded as a 32-bit word. To explain how this was done, we start with a single 0 and build up a matrix step by step by repeatedly carrying out the following step:

replicate what you have so far, both to the right and below, and fill in the gap with the same matrix, but with the numbers 0 and 1 interchanged.

So, to begin with, we get:

$$\begin{bmatrix} 0 & 0 \\ 0 & 1 \end{bmatrix}$$

Next, we get:

$$\begin{bmatrix} 0 & 0 & 0 & 0 \\ 0 & 1 & 0 & 1 \\ 0 & 0 & 1 & 1 \\ 0 & 1 & 1 & 0 \end{bmatrix}$$

and after one more stage, we get:

$$\begin{bmatrix} 0 & 0 & 0 & 0 & 0 & 0 & 0 & 0 \\ 0 & 1 & 0 & 1 & 0 & 1 & 0 & 1 \\ 0 & 0 & 1 & 1 & 0 & 0 & 1 & 1 \\ 0 & 1 & 1 & 0 & 0 & 1 & 1 & 0 \\ 0 & 0 & 0 & 0 & 1 & 1 & 1 & 1 \\ 0 & 1 & 0 & 1 & 1 & 0 & 1 & 0 \\ 0 & 0 & 1 & 1 & 1 & 1 & 0 & 0 \\ 0 & 1 & 1 & 0 & 1 & 0 & 0 & 1 \end{bmatrix}$$

Three more stages in this process yield a matrix that contains within it the code used by Mariner 9.

We now consider another way of arriving at these patterns. Starting with a row of 0s, we successively add in certain binary words. The first of these words is

$$\mathbf{c}_0 = \begin{bmatrix} 0 & 1 & 0 & 1 & 0 & 1 & 0 & 1 & 0 & 1 & 0 & 1 & 0 & 1 & 0 & 1 \end{bmatrix}$$

Taking the row of 0s, and then the same thing with c_0 added, we get:

$$\begin{matrix} \mathbf{0} \\ \mathbf{c}_0 \end{matrix} \begin{bmatrix} 0 & 0 & 0 & 0 & 0 & 0 & 0 & 0 & 0 & 0 & 0 & 0 & 0 & 0 & 0 & 0 \\ 0 & 1 & 0 & 1 & 0 & 1 & 0 & 1 & 0 & 1 & 0 & 1 & 0 & 1 & 0 & 1 \end{bmatrix}$$

The next word is:

$$\mathbf{c}_1 = \begin{bmatrix} 0 & 0 & 1 & 1 & 0 & 0 & 1 & 1 & 0 & 0 & 1 & 1 & 0 & 0 & 1 & 1 \end{bmatrix}$$

Taking what we have so far, and then the same thing with c_1 added to each row, we obtain the matrix

$$\begin{matrix} \mathbf{0} \\ \mathbf{c}_0 \\ \mathbf{c}_1 \\ \mathbf{c}_0 + \mathbf{c}_1 \end{matrix} \begin{bmatrix} 0 & 0 & 0 & 0 & 0 & 0 & 0 & 0 & 0 & 0 & 0 & 0 & 0 & 0 & 0 & 0 \\ 0 & 1 & 0 & 1 & 0 & 1 & 0 & 1 & 0 & 1 & 0 & 1 & 0 & 1 & 0 & 1 \\ 0 & 0 & 1 & 1 & 0 & 0 & 1 & 1 & 0 & 0 & 1 & 1 & 0 & 0 & 1 & 1 \\ 0 & 1 & 1 & 0 & 0 & 1 & 1 & 0 & 0 & 1 & 1 & 0 & 0 & 1 & 1 & 0 \end{bmatrix}$$

The next two words are

$$\mathbf{c}_2 = \begin{bmatrix} 0 & 0 & 0 & 0 & 1 & 1 & 1 & 1 & 0 & 0 & 0 & 0 & 1 & 1 & 1 & 1 \end{bmatrix}$$

and

$$\mathbf{c}_3 = \begin{bmatrix} 0 & 0 & 0 & 0 & 0 & 0 & 0 & 0 & 1 & 1 & 1 & 1 & 1 & 1 & 1 & 1 \end{bmatrix}$$

These two stages lead to a 16×16 array:

$$
\begin{array}{c}
\\
\mathbf{c}_0 \\
\mathbf{c}_1 \\
\\
\mathbf{c}_2 \\
\\
\\
\\
\mathbf{c}_3 \\
\\
\\
\\
\\
\\
\\
\\
\end{array}
\begin{bmatrix}
0 & 0 & 0 & 0 & 0 & 0 & 0 & 0 & 0 & 0 & 0 & 0 & 0 & 0 & 0 & 0 \\
0 & 1 & 0 & 1 & 0 & 1 & 0 & 1 & 0 & 1 & 0 & 1 & 0 & 1 & 0 & 1 \\
0 & 0 & 1 & 1 & 0 & 0 & 1 & 1 & 0 & 0 & 1 & 1 & 0 & 0 & 1 & 1 \\
0 & 1 & 1 & 0 & 0 & 1 & 1 & 0 & 0 & 1 & 1 & 0 & 0 & 1 & 1 & 0 \\
0 & 0 & 0 & 0 & 1 & 1 & 1 & 1 & 0 & 0 & 0 & 0 & 1 & 1 & 1 & 1 \\
0 & 1 & 0 & 1 & 1 & 0 & 1 & 0 & 0 & 1 & 0 & 1 & 1 & 0 & 1 & 0 \\
0 & 0 & 1 & 1 & 1 & 1 & 0 & 0 & 0 & 0 & 1 & 1 & 1 & 1 & 0 & 0 \\
0 & 1 & 1 & 0 & 1 & 0 & 0 & 1 & 0 & 1 & 1 & 0 & 1 & 0 & 0 & 1 \\
0 & 0 & 0 & 0 & 0 & 0 & 0 & 0 & 1 & 1 & 1 & 1 & 1 & 1 & 1 & 1 \\
0 & 1 & 0 & 1 & 0 & 1 & 0 & 1 & 1 & 0 & 1 & 1 & 0 & 0 & 1 & 0 \\
0 & 0 & 1 & 1 & 0 & 0 & 1 & 1 & 1 & 1 & 0 & 0 & 1 & 1 & 0 & 0 \\
0 & 1 & 1 & 0 & 0 & 1 & 1 & 0 & 1 & 0 & 0 & 1 & 1 & 0 & 0 & 1 \\
0 & 0 & 0 & 0 & 1 & 1 & 1 & 1 & 1 & 1 & 1 & 1 & 0 & 0 & 0 & 0 \\
0 & 1 & 0 & 1 & 1 & 0 & 1 & 0 & 1 & 0 & 1 & 0 & 0 & 1 & 0 & 1 \\
0 & 0 & 1 & 1 & 1 & 1 & 0 & 0 & 1 & 1 & 0 & 0 & 0 & 0 & 1 & 1 \\
0 & 1 & 1 & 0 & 1 & 0 & 0 & 1 & 1 & 0 & 0 & 1 & 0 & 1 & 1 & 0 \\
\end{bmatrix}
$$

We could go on in this way, generating larger and larger arrays. Each row is obtained from the row of 0s by adding in one or more of the c_i rows, and is thus of the form

$$\alpha_0 \mathbf{c}_0 + \alpha_1 \mathbf{c}_1 + \alpha_2 \mathbf{c}_2 + \alpha_3 \mathbf{c}_3,$$

where addition is modulo 2, and where each α_i is 1 if we include the corresponding $\mathbf{c}_i$, and 0 otherwise.

This gives the method of encoding: the four *data bits* α_0, α_1, α_2 and α_3 are encoded as a 16-bit word by using the above expression. For example, 1101 is encoded as

$$\mathbf{c}_0 + \mathbf{c}_1 + \mathbf{c}_3$$

which gives the 12th row

$$0\ 1\ 1\ 0\ 0\ 1\ 1\ 0\ 1\ 0\ 0\ 1\ 1\ 0\ 0\ 1.$$

Note that we can get a more efficient code by transmitting just the last eight bits of each row as the codeword:

$$
\begin{bmatrix}
0 & 0 & 0 & 0 & 0 & 0 & 0 & 0 \\
0 & 1 & 0 & 1 & 0 & 1 & 0 & 1 \\
0 & 0 & 1 & 1 & 0 & 0 & 1 & 1 \\
0 & 1 & 1 & 0 & 0 & 1 & 1 & 0 \\
0 & 0 & 0 & 0 & 1 & 1 & 1 & 1 \\
0 & 1 & 0 & 1 & 1 & 0 & 1 & 0 \\
0 & 0 & 1 & 1 & 1 & 1 & 0 & 0 \\
0 & 1 & 1 & 0 & 1 & 0 & 0 & 1 \\
1 & 1 & 1 & 1 & 1 & 1 & 1 & 1 \\
1 & 0 & 1 & 0 & 1 & 0 & 1 & 0 \\
1 & 1 & 0 & 0 & 1 & 1 & 0 & 0 \\
1 & 0 & 0 & 1 & 1 & 0 & 0 & 1 \\
1 & 1 & 1 & 1 & 0 & 0 & 0 & 0 \\
1 & 0 & 1 & 0 & 0 & 1 & 0 & 1 \\
1 & 1 & 0 & 0 & 0 & 0 & 1 & 1 \\
1 & 0 & 0 & 1 & 0 & 1 & 1 & 0 \\
\end{bmatrix}
$$

These are the 16 codewords of the code $\mathcal{R}(3)$. This code can detect up to 2 errors and correct 1 error.

Extending the pattern first to a 32×32 array, and then to a 64×64 array, and taking just the last 32 bits in each row, we get the 64 codewords of the code $\mathcal{R}(5)$. This was the code used by Mariner 9; it can detect up to 8 errors and correct up to 7 errors, and so is much more powerful than the code $\mathcal{R}(3)$.

To demonstrate just how effective these codes can be, we can set up a computer to simulate the noisy transmission. Stored within the computer is a large matrix of 0s and 1s. When this is printed out with a white dot for each 0-bit and a black dot for each 1-bit, it appears as a picture of a man's head.

There are more than 53 000 elements in the picture, and it is easier to see what is going on if we look at just 48 of them from somewhere in the centre of the picture.

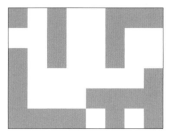

The digital representation of this is:

$$\begin{bmatrix} 1 & 0 & 1 & 0 & 0 & 1 & 1 & 1 \\ 0 & 0 & 1 & 0 & 0 & 1 & 0 & 0 \\ 1 & 0 & 1 & 0 & 0 & 1 & 0 & 0 \\ 1 & 0 & 0 & 0 & 0 & 0 & 0 & 1 \\ 1 & 0 & 0 & 0 & 1 & 1 & 1 & 1 \\ 1 & 1 & 1 & 1 & 0 & 1 & 0 & 1 \end{bmatrix}$$

When this is transmitted *without* encoding, the simulated noise introduces errors; what we receive is:

$$\begin{bmatrix} 1 & 0 & 0 & 0 & 0 & 1 & 1 & 1 \\ 0 & 0 & 1 & 0 & 0 & 1 & 0 & 0 \\ 0 & 0 & 1 & 0 & 0 & 1 & 0 & 0 \\ 1 & 0 & 0 & 0 & 1 & 0 & 1 & 1 \\ 1 & 0 & 0 & 0 & 1 & 0 & 1 & 1 \\ 1 & 1 & 1 & 1 & 0 & 1 & 0 & 1 \end{bmatrix}$$

In the absence of any error-free correction, these errors are all present in the picture:

If, instead, the groups of 4 bits are encoded (using $\mathcal{R}(3)$) as 8-bit codewords, so that our 48 bits become:

$$\begin{bmatrix}
1 & 1 & 0 & 0 & 1 & 1 & 0 & 0 & 0 & 1 & 1 & 0 & 1 & 0 & 0 & 1 \\
0 & 0 & 1 & 1 & 0 & 0 & 1 & 1 & 0 & 0 & 0 & 0 & 1 & 1 & 1 & 1 \\
1 & 1 & 0 & 0 & 1 & 1 & 0 & 0 & 0 & 0 & 0 & 0 & 1 & 1 & 1 & 1 \\
1 & 1 & 1 & 1 & 1 & 1 & 1 & 1 & 0 & 1 & 0 & 1 & 0 & 1 & 0 & 1 \\
1 & 1 & 1 & 1 & 1 & 1 & 1 & 1 & 1 & 0 & 0 & 1 & 0 & 1 & 1 & 0 \\
1 & 0 & 0 & 1 & 0 & 1 & 1 & 0 & 0 & 1 & 0 & 1 & 1 & 0 & 1 & 0
\end{bmatrix}$$

then noisy transmission *still* introduces errors:

$$\begin{bmatrix}
1 & 1 & 0 & 0 & 1 & 1 & 0 & 1 & 0 & 1 & 1 & 0 & 1 & 0 & 0 & 1 \\
0 & 0 & 1 & 1 & 0 & 0 & 1 & 1 & 0 & 0 & 1 & 0 & 1 & 1 & 1 & 1 \\
1 & 1 & 0 & 0 & 1 & 1 & 0 & 0 & 0 & 0 & 0 & 0 & 1 & 1 & 0 & 1 \\
1 & 1 & 1 & 1 & 1 & 1 & 1 & 1 & 0 & 1 & 0 & 1 & 0 & 1 & 0 & 1 \\
1 & 0 & 1 & 1 & 1 & 1 & 1 & 1 & 1 & 0 & 0 & 1 & 0 & 1 & 1 & 0 \\
1 & 0 & 0 & 1 & 0 & 1 & 1 & 0 & 0 & 1 & 0 & 0 & 1 & 0 & 0 & 1
\end{bmatrix}$$

However, most of these errors are corrected by the decoding procedure, and the resulting picture is much better than before:

So even $\mathcal{R}(3)$ can produce this marked improvement in picture quality. The Mariner 9 code $\mathcal{R}(5)$ can do very much better and, even with very noisy transmission conditions, produced some most remarkable pictures of Mars. It is said that a picture is worth a thousand words. As encoded by Mariner 9, these pictures are worth 873 600 words!

4.5 Computer activities

The computer activities for this section are described in the *Computer Activities Booklet*.

After studying this section, you should be able to:

- construct *the first-order Reed-Muller code* $\mathcal{R}(m)$ from the family of Boolean functions that are polynomials of degree at most 1 in m variables;

- write down the length, dimension and minimum distance of the first-order Reed-Muller code $\mathcal{R}(m)$;

- decode first-order Reed-Muller codes using a majority-logic decoding scheme;

- describe the construction of the Golay codes;

- outline the use of the Reed-Muller codes in the Mariner 9 space project.

---

5 Compact discs

This section is a television section on the design of compact discs. The programme is described in the related *Television Notes*.

Appendix (Optional)

Error Detecting and Error Correcting Codes

By R. W. HAMMING

1. INTRODUCTION

THE author was led to the study given in this paper from a consideration of large scale computing machines in which a large number of operations must be performed without a single error in the end result. This problem of "doing things right" on a large scale is not essentially new; in a telephone central office, for example, a very large number of operations are performed while the errors leading to wrong numbers are kept well under control, though they have not been completely eliminated. This has been achieved, in part, through the use of self-checking circuits. The occasional failure that escapes routine checking is still detected by the customer and will, if it persists, result in customer complaint, while if it is transient it will produce only occasional wrong numbers. At the same time the rest of the central office functions satisfactorily. In a digital computer, on the other hand, a single failure usually means the complete failure, in the sense that if it is detected no more computing can be done until the failure is located and corrected, while if it escapes detection then it invalidates all subsequent operations of the machine. Put in other words, in a telephone central office there are a number of parallel paths which are more or less independent of each other; in a digital machine there is usually a single long path which passes through the same piece of equipment many, many times before the answer is obtained.

In transmitting information from one place to another digital machines use codes which are simply sets of symbols to which meanings or values are attached. Examples of codes which were designed to detect isolated errors are numerous; among them are the highly developed 2 out of 5 codes used extensively in common control switching systems and in the Bell Relay Computers,[1] the 3 out of 7 code used for radio telegraphy,[2] and the word count sent at the end of telegrams.

In some situations self-checking is not enough. For example, in the Model 5 Relay Computers built by Bell Telephone Laboratories for the Aberdeen Proving Grounds,[1] observations in the early period indicated about two or three relay failures per day in the 8900 relays of the two computers, representing about one failure per two to three million relay operations. The self-checking feature meant that these failures did not introduce undetected errors. Since the machines were run on an unattended basis over nights and week-ends, however, the errors meant that frequently the computations came to a halt although often the machines took up new problems. The present trend is toward electronic speeds in digital computers where the basic elements are somewhat more reliable per operation than relays. However, the incidence of isolated failures, even when detected, may seriously interfere with the normal use of such machines. Thus it appears desirable to examine the next step beyond error detection, namely error correction.

We shall assume that the transmitting equipment handles information in the binary form of a sequence of 0's and 1's. This assumption is made both for mathematical convenience and because the binary system is the natural form for representing the open and closed relays, flip-flop circuits, dots and dashes, and perforated tapes that are used in many forms of communication. Thus each code symbol will be represented by a sequence of 0's and 1's.

The codes used in this paper are called *systematic* codes. Systematic codes may be defined[3] as codes in which each code symbol has exactly n binary digits, where m digits are associated with the information while the other $k = n - m$ digits are used for error detection and correction. This produces a *redundancy R* defined as the ratio of the number of binary digits used to the minimum number necessary to convey the same information, that is,

$$R = n/m.$$

This serves to measure the efficiency of the code as far as the transmission of information is concerned, and is the only aspect of the problem discussed in any detail here. The redundancy may be said to lower the effective channel capacity for sending information.

The need for error correction having assumed importance only recently, very little is known about the economics of the matter. It is clear that in using such codes there will be extra equipment for encoding and correcting errors as well as the lowered effective channel capacity referred to above. Because of these considerations applications of these codes may be expected to occur first only under extreme conditions. Some typical situations seem to be:

> a unattended operation over long periods of time with the minimum of standby equipment.
> b. extremely large and tightly interrelated systems where a single failure incapacitates the entire installation.
> c. signalling in the presence of noise where it is either impossible or uneconomical to reduce the effect of the noise on the signal.

These situations are occurring more and more often. The first two are particularly true of large scale digital computing machines, while the third occurs, among other places, in "jamming situations".

The principles for designing error detecting and correcting codes in the cases most likely to be applied first are given in this paper. Circuits for implementing these principles may be designed by the application of well-known techniques, but the problem is not discussed here. Part I of the paper shows how to construct special minimum redundancy codes in the following cases:

> a single error detecting codes
> b single error correcting codes
> c single error correcting plus double error detecting codes.

Part II discusses the general theory of such codes and proves that under the assumptions made the codes of Part I are the "best" possible.

PART I

SPECIAL CODES

2. SINGLE ERROR DETECTING CODES

We may construct a single error detecting code having n binary digits in the following manner: In the first $n - 1$ positions we put $n - 1$ digits of information. In the n-th position we place either 0 or 1, so that the entire n positions have an even number of 1's. This is clearly a single error detecting code since any single error in transmission would leave an odd number of 1's in a code symbol.

The redundancy of these codes is, since $m = n - 1$,

$$R = \frac{n}{n-1} = 1 + \frac{1}{n-1}.$$

It might appear that to gain a low redundancy we should let n become very large. However, by increasing n, the probability of at least one error in a symbol increases; and the risk of a double error, which would pass undetected, also increases. For example, if $p \ll 1$ is the probability of any error, then for n so large as $1/p$, the probability of a correct symbol is approximately $1/e = 0.3679 \ldots$, while a double error has probability $1/2e = 0.1839 \ldots$.

The type of check used above to determine whether or not the symbol has any single error will be used throughout the paper and will be called a *parity check*. The above was an *even* parity check; had we used an odd number of 1's to determine the setting of the check position it would have been an odd parity check. Furthermore, a parity check need not always involve all the positions of the symbol but may be a check over selected positions only.

---

[1] Franz Alt, "A Bell Telephone Laboratories' Computing Machine" — I, II. Mathematical Tables and other Aids to Computation, Vol. 3, pp. 1–13 and 60–84, Jan. and Apr., 1948.

[2] S. Sparks, and R. G. Kreer, "Tape Relay System for Radio Telegraph Operation" *R.C.A. Review*, Vol. 8, pp. 393–426, (especially p. 417), 1947.

[3] In Section 7 this is shown to be equivalent to a much weaker appearing definition.

Reprinted with permission from *Bell Syst. Tech. J.*, vol. 29, pp. 147–160, Apr. 1950. Copyright © 1950, American Telephone and Telegraph Company.

3. SINGLE ERROR CORRECTING CODES

To construct a single error correcting code we first assign m of the n available positions as information positions. We shall regard the m as fixed, but the specific positions are left to a later determination. We next assign the k remaining positions as check positions. The values in these k positions are to be determined in the encoding process by even parity checks over selected information positions.

Let us imagine for the moment that we have received a code symbol, with or without an error. Let us apply the k parity checks, in order, and for each time the parity check assigns the value observed in its check position we write a 0, while for each time the assigned and observed values disagree we write a 1. When written from right to left in a line this sequence of k 0's and 1's (to be distinguished from the values assigned by the parity checks) may be regarded as a binary number and will be called the *checking number*. We shall require that this checking number give the position of any single error, with the zero value meaning no error in the symbol. Thus the check number must describe $m + k + 1$ different things, so that

$$2^k \geq m + k + 1$$

is a condition on k. Writing $n = m + k$ we find

$$2^m \leq \frac{2^n}{n + 1}.$$

Using this inequality we may calculate Table 1, which gives the maximum m for a given n, or, what is the same thing, the minimum n for a given m.

TABLE I

n	m	Corresponding k
1	0	1
2	0	2
3	1	2
4	1	3
5	2	3
6	3	3
7	4	3
8	4	4
9	5	4
10	6	4
11	7	4
12	8	4
13	9	4
14	10	4
15	11	4
16	11	5
		Etc.

We now determine the positions over which each of the various parity checks is to be applied. The checking number is obtained digit by digit, from right to left, by applying the parity checks in order and writing down the corresponding 0 or 1 as the case may be. Since the checking number is to give the position of any error in a code symbol, any position which has a 1 on the right of its binary representation must cause the first check to fail. Examining the binary form of the various integers we find

$$
\begin{array}{rcl}
1 & = & \quad\quad\ 1 \\
3 & = & \quad\ 1\ 1 \\
5 & = & 1\ 0\ 1 \\
7 & = & 1\ 1\ 1 \\
9 & = & 1\ 0\ 0\ 1 \\
& & \text{Etc.}
\end{array}
$$

have a 1 on the extreme right. Thus the first parity check must use positions

$$1, 3, 5, 7, 9, \ldots .$$

In an exactly similar fashion we find that the second parity check must use those positions which have 1's for the second digit from the right of their binary representation,

$$
\begin{array}{rcl}
2 & = & \quad\quad 1\ 0 \\
3 & = & \quad\quad 1\ 1 \\
6 & = & \quad 1\ 1\ 0 \\
7 & = & \quad 1\ 1\ 1 \\
10 & = & 1\ 0\ 1\ 0 \\
11 & = & 1\ 0\ 1\ 1 \\
& & \text{Etc.}
\end{array}
$$

the third parity check

$$
\begin{array}{rcl}
4 & = & \quad\quad 1\ 0\ 0 \\
5 & = & \quad\quad 1\ 0\ 1 \\
6 & = & \quad\quad 1\ 1\ 0 \\
7 & = & \quad\quad 1\ 1\ 1 \\
12 & = & \quad 1\ 1\ 0\ 0 \\
13 & = & \quad 1\ 1\ 0\ 1 \\
14 & = & \quad 1\ 1\ 1\ 0 \\
15 & = & \quad 1\ 1\ 1\ 1 \\
20 & = & 1\ 0\ 1\ 0\ 0 \\
& & \text{Etc.}
\end{array}
$$

It remains to decide for each parity check which positions are to contain information and which the check. The choice of the positions 1, 2, 4, 8, ... for check positions, as given in the following table, has the advantage of making the setting of the check positions independent of each other. All other positions are information positions. Thus we obtain Table II.

TABLE II

Check Number	Check Positions	Positions Checked
1	1	1, 3, 5, 7, 9, 11, 13, 15, 17, ...
2	2	2, 3, 6, 7, 10, 11, 14, 15, 18, ...
3	4	4, 5, 6, 7, 12, 13, 14, 15, 20, ...
4	8	8, 9, 10, 11, 12, 13, 14, 15, 24, ...
.	.	.
.	.	.
.	.	.

As an illustration of the above theory we apply it to the case of a seven-position code. From Table I we find for $n = 7$, $m = 4$ and $k = 3$. From Table II we find that the first parity check involves positions 1, 3, 5, 7 and is used to determine the value in the first position; the second parity check, positions 2, 3, 6, 7, and determines the value in the second position; and the third parity check, positions 4, 5, 6, 7, and determines the value in position four. This leaves positions 3, 5, 6, 7 as information positions. The results of writing down all possible binary numbers using positions 3, 5, 6, 7, and then calculating the values in the check positions 1, 2, 4, are shown in Table III.

Thus a seven-position single error correcting code admits of 16 code symbols. There are, of course $2^7 - 16 = 112$ meaningless symbols. In some applications it may be desirable to drop the first symbol from the code to avoid the all zero combination as either a code symbol or a code symbol plus a single error, since this might be confused with no message. This would still leave 15 useful code symbols.

TABLE III

Position							Decimal Value of Symbol
1	2	3	4	5	6	7	
0	0	0	0	0	0	0	0
1	1	0	1	0	0	1	1
0	1	0	1	0	1	0	2
1	0	0	0	0	1	1	3
1	0	0	1	1	0	0	4
0	1	0	0	1	0	1	5
1	1	0	0	1	1	0	6
0	0	0	1	1	1	1	7
1	1	1	0	0	0	0	8
0	0	1	1	0	0	1	9
1	0	1	1	0	1	0	10
0	1	1	0	0	1	1	11
0	1	1	1	1	0	0	12
1	0	1	0	1	0	1	13
0	0	1	0	1	1	0	14
1	1	1	1	1	1	1	15

As an illustration of how this code "works" let us take the symbol 0 1 1 1 1 0 0 corresponding to the decimal value 12 and change the 1 in the fifth position to a 0. We now examine the new symbol

$$0\ 1\ 1\ 1\ 0\ 0\ 0$$

by the methods of this section to see how the error is located. From Table II the first parity check is over positions 1, 3, 5, 7 and predicts a 1 for the first position while we find a 0 there; hence we write a

$$1\ .$$

The second parity check is over positions 2, 3, 6, 7, and predicts the second position correctly; hence we write a 0 to the left of the 1, obtaining

$$0\ 1\ .$$

The third parity check is over positions 4, 5, 6, 7 and predicts wrongly; hence we write a 1 to the left of the 0 1, obtaining

$$1\ 0\ 1\ .$$

This sequence of 0's and 1's regarded as a binary number is the number 5; hence the error is in the fifth position. The correct symbol is therefore obtained by changing the 0 in the fifth position to a 1.

4. SINGLE ERROR CORRECTING PLUS DOUBLE ERROR DETECTING CODES

To construct a single error correcting plus double error detecting code we begin with a single error correcting code. To this code we add one more position for checking all the previous positions, using an even parity check. To see the operation of this code we have to examine a number of cases:

1. No errors. All parity checks, including the last, are satisfied.
2. Single error. The last parity check fails in all such situations whether the error be in the information, the original check positions, or the last check position. The original checking number gives the position of the error, where now the zero value means the last check position.
3. Two errors. In all such situations the last parity check is satisfied, and the checking number indicates some kind of error.

As an illustration let us construct an eight-position code from the previous seven-position code. To do this we add an eighth position which is chosen so that there are an even number of 1's in the eight positions. Thus we add an eighth column to Table III which has:

TABLE IV

0
0
1
1
1
1
0
0
1
1
0
0
0
1
1

PART II

GENERAL THEORY

5. A GEOMETRICAL MODEL

When examining various problems connected with error detecting and correcting codes it is often convenient to introduce a geometric model. The model used here consists in identifying the various sequences of 0's and 1's which are the symbols of a code with vertices of a unit n-dimensional cube. The code points, labelled $x, y, z, ...$, form a subset of the set of all vertices of the cube.

Into this space of 2^n points we introduce a *distance*, or, as it is usually called, a *metric*, $D(x, y)$. The definition of the metric is based on the observation that a single error in a code point changes one coordinate, two errors, two coordinates, and in general d errors produce a difference in d coordinates. Thus we define the distance $D(x, y)$ between two points x and y as the number of coordinates for which x and y are different. This is the same as the least number of edges which must be traversed in going from x to y. This distance function satisfies the usual three conditions for a metric, namely,

$$D(x, y) = 0 \quad \text{if and only if } x = y$$
$$D(x, y) = D(y, x) > 0 \quad \text{if } x \neq y$$
$$D(x, y) + D(y, z) \geq D(x, z) \text{ (triangle inequality).}$$

As an example we note that each of the following code points in the three-dimensional cube is two units away from the others,

$$\begin{array}{ccc} 0 & 0 & 1 \\ 0 & 1 & 0 \\ 1 & 0 & 0 \\ 1 & 1 & 1 \end{array}$$

To continue the geometric language, a sphere of radius r about a point x defined as all points which are at a distance r from the point x. Thus, in the above example, the first three code points are on a sphere of radius 2 about the point $(1, 1, 1)$. In fact, in this example any one code point may be chosen as the centre and the other three will lie on the surface of a sphere of radius 2.

If all the code points are at a distance of at least 2 from each other then it follows that any single error will carry a code point over to a point that is not a code point, and hence is a meaningless symbol. This in turn means that any single error is detectable. If the minimum distance between code points is at least three units then any single error will leave the point nearer to the correct code point than to any other code point, and this means that any single error will be correctable. This type of information is summarized in the following table:

TABLE V

Minimum distance	Meaning
1	uniqueness
2	single error detection
3	single error correction
4	single error correction plus double error detection
5	double error correction
	Etc.

Conversely, it is evident that, if we are to effect the detection and correction listed, then all the distances between code points must equal or exceed the minimum distance listed. Thus the problem of finding suitable codes is the same as that of finding subsets of points in the space which maintain at least the minimum distance condition. The special codes in sections 2, 3, and 4 were merely descriptions of how to choose a particular subset of points for minimum distances 2, 3, and 4 respectively.

It should perhaps be noted that, at a given minimum distance, some of the correctability may be exchanged for more detectability. For example, a subset with minimum distance 5 may be used for:

  a   double error correction, (with, of course, double error detection).
  b.   single error correction plus triple error detection.
  c.   quadruple error detection.

Returning for the moment to the particular codes constructed in Part I we note that any interchanges of positions in a code do not change the code in any essential way. Neither does interchanging the 0's and 1's in any position, a process usually called complementing. This idea is made more precise in the following definition:

Definition. Two codes are said to be *equivalent* to each other if, by a finite number of the following operations, one can be transformed into the other:

  1.   The interchange of any two positions in the code symbols.
  2.   The complementing of the values in any position in the code symbols. This is a formal equivalence relation ($\sim$) since $A \sim A$; $A \sim B$ implies $B \sim A$; and $A \sim B, B \sim C$ implies $A \sim C$. Thus we can reduce the study of a class of codes to the study of typical members of each equivalence class.

In terms of the geometric model, equivalence transformations amount to rotations and reflections of the unit cube.

6.   SINGLE ERROR DETECTING CODES

The problem studied in this section is that of packing the maximum number of points in a unit n-dimensional cube such that no two points are closer than 2 units from each other. We shall show that, as in section 2 2^{n-1} points can be so packed, and, further, that any such optimal packing is equivalent to that used in section 2.

To prove these statements we first observe that the vertices of the n-dimensional cube are composed of those of two $(n-1)$-dimensional cubes. Let A be the maximum number of points packed in the original cube. Then one of the two $(n-1)$-dimensional cubes has at least $A/2$ points. This cube being again decomposed into two lower dimensional cubes, we find that one of them has at least $A/2^2$ points. Continuing in this way we come to a two-dimensional cube having $A/2^{n-2}$ points. We now observe that a square can have at most two points separated by at least two units; hence the original n-dimensional cube had at most 2^{n-1} points not less than two units apart.

To prove the equivalence of any two optimal packings we note that, if the packing is optimal, then each of the two sub-cubes has half the points. Calling this the first coordinate we see that half the points have a 0 and half have a 1. The next subdivision will again divide these into two equal groups having 0's

and 1's respectively. After $(n-1)$ such stages we have, upon reordering the assigned values if there be any, exactly the first $n-1$ positions of the code devised in section 2. To each sequence of the first $n-1$ coordinates there exist $n-1$ other sequences which differ from it by one coordinate. Once we fix the n-th coordinate of some one point, say the origin which has all 0's, then to maintain the known minimum distance of two units between code points the n-th coordinate is uniquely determined for all other code points. Thus the last coordinate is determined within a complementation so that any optimal code is equivalent to that given in section 2.

It is interesting to note that in these two proofs we have used only the assumption that the code symbols are all of length n.

7.   SINGLE ERROR CORRECTING CODES

It has probably been noted by the reader that, in the particular codes of Part I, a distinction was made between information and check positions, while, in the geometric model, there is no real distinction between the various coordinates. To bring the two treatments more in line with each other we redefine a *systematic* code as a code whose symbol lengths are all equal and

  1.   The positions checked are independent of the information contained in the symbol.
  2.   The checks are independent of each other.
  3.   We use parity checks.

This is equivalent to the earlier definition. To show this we form a matrix whose i-th row has 1's in the positions of the i-th parity check and 0's elsewhere. By assumption 1 the matrix is fixed and does not change from code symbol to code symbol. From 2 the rank of the matrix is k. This in turn means that the system can be solved for k of the positions expressed in terms of the other $n-k$ positions. Assumption 3 indicates that in this solving we use the arithmetic in which $1 + 1 = 0$.

There exist non-systematic codes, but so far none have been found which for a given n and minimum distance d have more code symbols than a systematic code. Section 9 gives an example of a non-systematic code.

Turning to the main problem of this section we find from Table V that a single error correcting code has code points at least three units from each other. Thus each point may be surrounded by a sphere of radius 1 with no two spheres having a point in common. Each sphere has a center point and n points on its surface, a total of $n + 1$ points. Thus the space of 2^n points can have at most:

$$\frac{2^n}{n+1}$$

spheres. This is exactly the bound we found before in section 3.

While we have shown that the special single error correcting code constructed in section 3 is of minimum redundancy, we cannot show that all optimal codes are equivalent, since the following trivial example shows that this is not so. For $n = 4$ we find from Table I that $m = 1$ and $k = 3$. Thus there are at most two code symbols in a four-position code. The following two optimal codes are clearly not equivalent:

$$
\begin{array}{cccc}
0 & 0 & 0 & 0 \\
1 & 1 & 1 & 1
\end{array}
\quad \text{and} \quad
\begin{array}{cccc}
0 & 0 & 0 & 0. \\
0 & 1 & 1 & 1.
\end{array}
$$

8.   SINGLE ERROR CORRECTING PLUS DOUBLE ERROR DETECTING CODES

In this section we shall prove that the codes constructed in section 4 are of minimal redundancy. We have already shown in section 4 how, for a minimum redundancy code of $n-1$ dimensions with a minimum distance of 3, we can construct an n dimensional code having the same number of code symbols but with a minimum distance of 4. If this were not of minimum redundancy there would exist a code having more code symbols but with the same n and the same minimum distance 4 between them. Taking this code we remove the last coordinate. This reduces the dimension from n to $n-1$ and the minimum distance between code symbols by, at most, one unit, while leaving the number of code symbols the same. This contradicts the assumption that the code we began our construction with was of minimum redundancy. Thus the codes of section 4 are of minimum redundancy.

This is a special case of the following general theorem: To any minimum redundancy code of N points in $n - 1$ dimensions and having a minimum distance of $2k - 1$ there corresponds a minimum redundancy code of N points in n dimensions having a minimum distance of $2k$, and conversely. To construct the n dimensional code from the $n - 1$ dimensional code we simply add a single n-th coordinate which is fixed by an even parity check over the n positions. This also increases the minimum distance by 1 for the following reason: Any two points which, in the $n - 1$ dimensional code, were at a distance $2k - 1$ from each other had an odd number of differences between their coordinates. Thus the parity check was set oppositely for the two points, increasing the distance between them to $2k$. The additional coordinate could not decrease any distances, so that all points in the code are now at a minimum distance of $2k$. To go in the reverse direction we simply drop one coordinate from the n dimensional code. This reduces the minimum distance of $2k$ to $2k - 1$ while leaving N the same. It is clear that if one code is of minimum redundancy then the other is, too.

9. MISCELLANEOUS OBSERVATIONS

For the next case, minimum distance of five units, one can surround each code point by a sphere of radius 2. Each sphere will contain

$$1 + C(n, 1) + C(n, 2)$$

points, where $C(n, k)$ is the binomial coefficient, so that an upper bound on the number of code points in a systematic code is

$$\frac{2^n}{1 + C(n, 1) + C(n, 2)} = \frac{2^{n+1}}{n^2 + n + 2} \leq 2^m.$$

This bound is too high. For example, in the case of $n = 7$, we find that $m = 2$ so that there should be a code with four code points. The maximum possible, as can be easily found by trial and error, is two.

In a similar fashion a bound on the number of code points may be found whenever the minimum distance between code points is an odd number. A bound on the even cases can then be found by use of the general theorem of the preceding section. These bounds are, in general, too high, as the above example shows.

If we write the bound on the number of code points in a unit cube of dimension n and with minimum distance d between them as $B(n, d)$ then the information of this type in the present paper may be summarized as follows:

$$B(n, 1) = 2^n$$

$$B(n, 2) = 2^{n-1}$$

$$B(n, 3) = 2^m \leq \frac{2^n}{n + 1}$$

$$B(n, 4) = 2^m \leq \frac{2^{n-1}}{n}$$

$$B(n - 1, 2k - 1) = B(n, 2k)$$

$$B(n, 2k - 1) = 2^m \leq \frac{2^n}{1 + C(n, 1) + \cdots + C(n, k - 1)}.$$

While these bounds have been attained for certain cases, no general methods have yet been found for constructing optimal codes when the minimum distance between code points exceeds four units, nor is it known whether the bound is or is not attainable by systematic codes.

We have dealt mainly with systematic codes. The existence of non-systematic codes is proved by the following example of a single error correcting code with $n = 6$.

$$
\begin{array}{cccccc}
0 & 0 & 0 & 0 & 0 & 0 \\
0 & 1 & 0 & 1 & 0 & 1 \\
1 & 0 & 0 & 1 & 1 & 0 \\
1 & 1 & 1 & 0 & 0 & 0 \\
0 & 0 & 1 & 0 & 1 & 1 \\
1 & 1 & 1 & 1 & 1 & 1 \\
\end{array}
$$

The all 0 symbol indicates that any parity check must be an even one. The all 1 symbol indicates that each parity check must involve an even number of positions. A direct comparison indicates that since no two columns are the same the even parity checks must involve four or six positions. An examination of the second symbol, which has three 1's in it, indicates that no six-position parity check can exist. Trying now the four-position parity checks we find that

$$
\begin{array}{ccccc}
1 & 2 & & 5 & 6 \\
& 2 & 3 & 4 & 5 \\
\end{array}
$$

are two independent parity checks and that no third one is independent of these two. Two parity checks can at most locate four positions, and, since there are six positions in the code, these two parity checks are not enough to locate any single error. The code is, however, single error correcting since it satisfies the minimum distance condition of three units.

The only previous work in the field of error correction that has appeared in print, so far as the author is aware. is that of M. J. E. Golay. [4]

[4] M. J. E. Golay, Correspondence, Notes on Digital Coding, *Proceedings of the I.R.E.*, Vol. 37, p. 657, June 1949.

Further reading

An elementary account of coding theory may be found in:

N. J. A. Sloane, *A Short Course on Error-correcting Codes*, (lectures at CISM, Udine, 1973), Springer-Verlag, New York, 1975

and in:

V.Pless, *Introduction to the Theory of Error-correcting Codes*, Wiley-Interscience, 1981.

The following are really mathematics books, but contain descriptions of digital switching circuits:

F. J. MacWilliams and N. J. A Sloane, *Theory of Error-correcting Codes*, North-Holland Publ. Co., Amsterdam, 1978.

W.W Peterson and E. J. Weldon, *Error-correcting Codes*, 2nd. ed., MIT Press, 1972.

Chapters 1, 3, 4 and 5 of the following book should be of interst to mathematicians — and within their reach:

D.Wiggert, *Error-control Coding and Applications*, Artech House Ltd., 1978.

The following books are suitable for readers with a solid mathematical background:

J. H. van Lint, *Introduction to Coding Theory*, Graduate Texts in Mathematics **86**, Springer-Verlag, New York, 1982.

P. J. Cameron and J. H. van Lint, *Designs, Graphs, Codes and their Links*, London Mathematical Society, Student Texts **22**, Cambridge University Press, 1991.

A discussion of convolutional codes may be found in Chapter 9 of the following book; students who have studied elementary probability theory will also find the Introduction well worth reading:

R. J. McEliece, *The Theory of Information and Coding*, Addison-Wesley, Reading, Mass., 1977.

Chapter 6 'Statistical Communication Theory of Digital Communications' of the following book may be of interest to technology students:

M. Schwartz, *Information Transmission, Modulation, and Noise*, 3rd. ed., McGraw-Hill, New York, 1980.

The following articles may also be of interest; the first describes the switching circuits for coding and decoding cyclic codes:

R. T. Chien, Memory Error Control: Beyond Parity, *IEEE Spectrum*, 18 – 23, July 1973.

K. I. Nordling, Error Control: Keeping Messages Clean, *Basics of Data Communications*, 169 – 173, McGraw-Hill, New York, 1976.

Exercises

In the following exercises, codes *A*, *B* and *C* are as follows.

code *A*	code *B*	code *C*
0000	0000000	00000000
0110	1110100	00001100
1111	0111010	00010100
1001	1001110	00011000
	1011001	00100100
	0101101	00101000
	1100011	00110000
	0010111	00111100
		11000011
		11001111
		11010111
		11011011
		11100111
		11101011
		11110011
		11111111

Section 1

1.1   Write down the length, dimension and rate of codes *A*, *B* and *C*.

1.2   Are the following encoding rules systematic?

(a)

message	codeword
0 0 0	00000
0 0 1	11001
0 1 0	00100
0 1 1	11101
1 0 0	10010
1 0 1	01101
1 1 0	11010
1 1 1	11111

(b)

message	codeword	message	codeword
0 0 0 0	0000000	1 0 0 0	0001011
0 0 0 1	0010111	1 0 0 1	0011100
0 0 1 0	0100110	1 0 1 0	0101101
0 0 1 1	0110001	1 0 1 1	0111010
0 1 0 0	1000101	1 1 0 0	1001110
0 1 0 1	1010010	1 1 0 1	1011001
0 1 1 0	1100011	1 1 1 0	1101000
0 1 1 1	1110100	1 1 1 1	1111111

1.3   Write down the Hamming distance between the binary words

(a)   01101 and 11000;

(b)   0011010 and 0011110;

(c)   11010100 and 00101011.

1.4 Write down the minimum distance δ of the code

{01010110

00110011

01010011

00110110}

1.5 How many errors are detected and corrected by

(a) a code with minimum distance 19?

(b) a code with minimum distance 20?

(c) codes *A*, *B* and *C*?

1.6 From each of the following codes, a codeword was transmitted and the binary word 1001111 was received. Use maximum likelihood decoding to find the transmitted codewords:

(a) {0000000, 1101001, 0101010 1000011,

1001100, 0100101, 1100110, 0001111,

1110000, 0011001, 1011010, 0110011,

0111100, 1010101, 0010110, 1111111};

(b) {0000000, 0010111, 0100110, 0110001,

1000101, 1010010, 1100011, 1110100,

0001011, 0011100, 0101101, 0111010,

1001110, 1011001, 1101000, 1111111}.

Section 2

2.1

(a) Add the binary words 011011 and 101010.

(b) The binary word 011011 is transmitted and affected by errors in the second, third and fifth bits. What is the error word, and which word is received?

(c) The codeword 101010 is transmitted and received as 110001. Which bits have been affected, and what is the error word?

2.2 Show that the following list of codewords is not a linear code:

00000

10101

01010

10001

01110

11011

11111

2.3 Are codes *A*, *B* and *C* linear ?

2.4

(a) Write down a generator set and a generator matrix for each of codes *A*, *B* and *C*. Is your matrix in standard form?

(b) Use the generator matrices you found in part (a) to encode the following messages:

01	for code *A*
110	for code *B*
1101	for code *C*.

In each case, check that your answer is a codeword of the original code.

2.5 Write down the parity check equations and a parity check matrix for each of the following codes:

(a) the 6-fold repetition code $R(6)$;

(b) {000000, 001110, 010101, 011011, 100011, 101101, 110110, 111000}.

2.6 For each code in Exercise 2.5, find the error syndrome of the received word 110101, and hence find the word most likely to have been transmitted.

2.7

(a) Write down a parity check matrix for each of the codes A, B and C.

(b) Find the error syndrome of the received word 1010101 for code B? Which word is most likely to have been transmitted?

2.8

(a) Is there a (31, 26, 3) linear code?

(b) Is there a (31, 23, 5) linear code?

In each case, if such a code exists, construct a parity check matrix; if no such code exists, explain why not.

Section 3

3.1 Are the following codes equivalent to codes A, B and C, respectively?

(a)	(b)	(c)
0000	0000000	00000000
0101	0011101	00001111
1010	0101011	00110011
1111	0110110	01010101
	1000111	01100110
	1011010	01011010
	1101100	00111100
	1110001	01101001
		11111111
		11110000
		11001100
		10101010
		10011001
		10100101
		11000011
		10010110

3.2 Which of the codes A, B and C and the three codes in Exercise 3.1 are cyclic?

3.3 Show that the following code is not cyclic, but is equivalent to a cyclic code.

{0101010, 1001100, 0011001, 1110000, 0100101, 1000011, 0010110}

3.4 What is the connection between the generator matrices and parity check matrices found in Exercises 2.4 and 2.7?

3.5

(a) Construct the extended code obtained from the following code:

{0000000, 1101001, 0101010, 1000011,
1001100, 0100101, 1100110, 0001111,
1110000, 0011001, 1011010, 0110011,
0111100, 1010101, 0010110, 1111111}.

(b) Write down the minimum distances and parity check matrices of the original and extended codes in part (a).

3.6

(a) Use the [**a** | **a** + **b**] construction to construct two codes of length 8 from the codes

$$\{0000, 0101, 1010, 1111\} \text{ and } \{0000, 1100, 0011, 1111\}.$$

(b) Write down the minimum distance, a parity check matrix and a generator matrix for each of these new codes.

Section 4

4.1

(a) Write down the length, dimension and minimum distance of each of the codes $\mathcal{R}(6)$ and $\mathcal{R}(7)$.

(b) How many errors does each code detect and correct?

4.2

(a) Explain how you would find the codewords of $\mathcal{R}(4)$.

(b) How would you use the codewords of $\mathcal{R}(4)$ to obtain the codewords of $\mathcal{R}(5)$?

4.3 Use the generator matrix of $\mathcal{R}(4)$ given in the text to:

(a) encode the messages 10001 and 11010;

(b) decode the received word 1100101101000011.

Solutions to the exercises

1.1 Code A has length 4, dimension 2 (since there are 2^2 codewords), and rate $2/4 = 1/2$.

Code B has length 7, dimension 3 (since there are 2^3 codewords), and rate $3/7$.

Code C has length 8, dimension 4 (since there are 2^4 codewords), and rate $4/8 = 1/2$.

1.2

(a) The encoding rule is not systematic.

One way of seeing this is to look at the messages 011 and 101. Since 011 corresponds to the codeword 11101, the *first* message bit should always appear in the *fourth* place in the corresponding codeword. But the first message bit of 101 does not appear in the fourth place of the corresponding codeword 01101, and so the encoding rule is not systematic.

(b) The encoding rule is systematic; the message bits appear in the fourth, first, second and third places of the corresponding codeword.

1.3

(a) 3; (b) 1; (c) 8.

1.4 The distance between each pair of codewords is either 2 or 4, so the minimum distance $\delta = 2$.

1.5

(a) By Theorem 1.1, the code can detect and correct up to $(19-1)/2 = 9$ errors.

(b) By Theorem 1.1, the code can detect up to $20/2 = 10$ errors and correct up to $(20-2)/2 = 9$ errors.

(c) For codes A and C, $\delta = 2$, so, by Theorem 1.1, each of these codes can detect up to one error but correct no errors; for code B, $\delta = 4$, so code B can detect up to two errors and correct up to one error .

1.6

(a) Inspecting the codewords, we see that 0001111 is at Hamming distance 1 from the received word; so this is the codeword most likely to have been transmitted.

(b) Inspecting the codewords, we see that 1001110 is at Hamming distance 1 from the received word; so this is the codeword most likely to have been transmitted.

2.1

(a) 110001.

(b) The error word is 011010; the received word is 000001.

(c) The second, third, fifth and sixth bits have been affected, and the error word is 011011.

2.2 If the code is linear, then the sum 00100 of the codewords 01010 and 01110 is also a codeword. On adding this codeword to the list, we do, in fact, obtain a linear code.

2.3 Codes A, B and C are all linear codes, since in each case the sum of any two codewords is also a codeword.

2.4

(a) There are several possibilities — for example:

Code A:

generator set $\langle 0110, 1001 \rangle$;

generator matrix $\begin{bmatrix} 0 & 1 & 1 & 0 \\ 1 & 0 & 0 & 1 \end{bmatrix}$

Taking the codewords in the reverse order would put the matrix into standard form.

Code B:

generator set $\langle 0010111, 0101101, 1001110 \rangle$;

generator matrix $\begin{bmatrix} 0 & 0 & 1 & 0 & 1 & 1 & 1 \\ 0 & 1 & 0 & 1 & 1 & 0 & 1 \\ 1 & 0 & 0 & 1 & 1 & 1 & 0 \end{bmatrix}$

Once again, taking the codewords in the reverse order would put the matrix into standard form.

Code C:

generator set $\langle 00100100, 00101000, 0011000, 11000011 \rangle$;

generator matrix $\begin{bmatrix} 0 & 0 & 1 & 0 & 0 & 1 & 0 & 0 \\ 0 & 0 & 1 & 0 & 1 & 0 & 0 & 0 \\ 0 & 0 & 1 & 1 & 0 & 0 & 0 & 0 \\ 1 & 1 & 0 & 0 & 0 & 0 & 1 & 1 \end{bmatrix}$

This matrix is not in standard form.

(b)

Code A:

$\begin{bmatrix} 0 & 1 \end{bmatrix} \begin{bmatrix} 0 & 1 & 1 & 0 \\ 1 & 0 & 0 & 1 \end{bmatrix} = \begin{bmatrix} 1 & 0 & 0 & 1 \end{bmatrix}$

Code B:

$\begin{bmatrix} 1 & 1 & 0 \end{bmatrix} \begin{bmatrix} 0 & 0 & 1 & 0 & 1 & 1 & 1 \\ 0 & 1 & 0 & 1 & 1 & 0 & 1 \\ 1 & 0 & 0 & 1 & 1 & 1 & 0 \end{bmatrix} = \begin{bmatrix} 0 & 1 & 1 & 1 & 0 & 1 & 0 \end{bmatrix}$

Code C:

$\begin{bmatrix} 1 & 1 & 0 & 1 \end{bmatrix} \begin{bmatrix} 0 & 0 & 1 & 0 & 0 & 1 & 0 & 0 \\ 0 & 0 & 1 & 0 & 1 & 0 & 0 & 0 \\ 0 & 0 & 1 & 1 & 0 & 0 & 0 & 0 \\ 1 & 1 & 0 & 0 & 0 & 0 & 1 & 1 \end{bmatrix} = \begin{bmatrix} 1 & 1 & 0 & 0 & 1 & 1 & 1 & 1 \end{bmatrix}$

In each case, the answer is a codeword of the original code.

2.5

(a) The code $R(6)$ is a $(6, 1)$ code; a parity check matrix is therefore a 5×6 matrix.

The bits of each codeword $\mathbf{x}$ of $R(6)$ satisfy the equations

$$
\begin{aligned}
x_1 + x_2 &&&&&= 0 \text{ (modulo 2)} \\
x_1 &&+ x_3 &&&= 0 \text{ (modulo 2)} \\
x_1 &&&+ x_4 &&= 0 \text{ (modulo 2)} \\
x_1 &&&&+ x_5 &= 0 \text{ (modulo 2)} \\
x_1 &&&&&+ x_6 = 0 \text{ (modulo 2)}
\end{aligned}
$$

There are other possibilities — for example, $x_2 + x_3 = 0$ (modulo 2).

The corresponding parity check matrix is

$$
\mathbf{H} = \begin{bmatrix}
1 & 1 & 0 & 0 & 0 & 0 \\
1 & 0 & 1 & 0 & 0 & 0 \\
1 & 0 & 0 & 1 & 0 & 0 \\
1 & 0 & 0 & 0 & 1 & 0 \\
1 & 0 & 0 & 0 & 0 & 1
\end{bmatrix}
$$

(b) The given code is a $(6, 3)$ code; a parity check matrix is therefore a 3×6 matrix.

The bits of each codeword $\mathbf{x}$ satisfy the equations

$$
\begin{aligned}
x_1 + x_2 &&&&+ x_6 &= 0 \text{ (modulo 2)} \\
x_1 + &&x_3 &+ x_5 &&= 0 \text{ (modulo 2)} \\
&x_2 + &x_3 + x_4 &&&= 0 \text{ (modulo 2)}
\end{aligned}
$$

Again, there are other possibilities — for example, $x_4 + x_5 + x_6 = 0$ (modulo 2).

The corresponding parity check matrix is

$$
\mathbf{H} = \begin{bmatrix}
1 & 1 & 0 & 0 & 0 & 1 \\
1 & 0 & 1 & 0 & 1 & 0 \\
0 & 1 & 1 & 1 & 0 & 0
\end{bmatrix}
$$

2.6

(a) For the code $R(6)$, the error syndrome $\mathbf{Hr}^T$ is

$$
\begin{bmatrix}
1 & 1 & 0 & 0 & 0 & 0 \\
1 & 0 & 1 & 0 & 0 & 0 \\
1 & 0 & 0 & 1 & 0 & 0 \\
1 & 0 & 0 & 0 & 1 & 0 \\
1 & 0 & 0 & 0 & 0 & 1
\end{bmatrix}
\begin{bmatrix} 1 \\ 1 \\ 0 \\ 1 \\ 0 \\ 1 \end{bmatrix}
=
\begin{bmatrix} 0 \\ 1 \\ 0 \\ 1 \\ 0 \end{bmatrix}
$$

This vector is the sum of the third and fifth columns of $\mathbf{H}$, so we suspect that 111111 was sent, and that x_3 and x_5 were corrupted.

(b) For this code, the error syndrome $\mathbf{Hr}^T$ is

$$
\begin{bmatrix}
1 & 1 & 0 & 0 & 0 & 1 \\
1 & 0 & 1 & 0 & 1 & 0 \\
0 & 1 & 1 & 1 & 0 & 0
\end{bmatrix}
\begin{bmatrix} 1 \\ 1 \\ 0 \\ 1 \\ 0 \\ 1 \end{bmatrix}
=
\begin{bmatrix} 1 \\ 1 \\ 0 \end{bmatrix}
$$

This vector is the first column of $\mathbf{H}$, so we suspect that 010101 was sent, and that x_1 was corrupted.

2.7

(a) There are various possible solutions — for example,

$$\mathbf{H}_A = \begin{bmatrix} 1 & 0 & 0 & 1 \\ 0 & 1 & 1 & 0 \end{bmatrix}$$

$$\mathbf{H}_B = \begin{bmatrix} 1 & 1 & 0 & 1 & 0 & 0 & 0 \\ 1 & 1 & 1 & 0 & 1 & 0 & 0 \\ 1 & 0 & 1 & 0 & 0 & 1 & 0 \\ 0 & 1 & 1 & 0 & 0 & 0 & 1 \end{bmatrix}$$

$$\mathbf{H}_C = \begin{bmatrix} 1 & 1 & 0 & 0 & 0 & 0 & 0 & 0 \\ 1 & 0 & 0 & 0 & 0 & 0 & 1 & 0 \\ 0 & 0 & 0 & 0 & 0 & 0 & 1 & 1 \\ 0 & 0 & 1 & 1 & 1 & 1 & 0 & 0 \end{bmatrix}$$

(b) The error syndrome $\mathbf{H}_B \mathbf{r}^T$ is

$$\begin{bmatrix} 1 & 1 & 0 & 1 & 0 & 0 & 0 \\ 1 & 1 & 1 & 0 & 1 & 0 & 0 \\ 1 & 0 & 1 & 0 & 0 & 1 & 0 \\ 0 & 1 & 1 & 0 & 0 & 0 & 1 \end{bmatrix} \begin{bmatrix} 1 \\ 0 \\ 1 \\ 0 \\ 1 \\ 0 \\ 1 \end{bmatrix} = \begin{bmatrix} 1 \\ 1 \\ 0 \\ 0 \end{bmatrix}$$

In this case, there are several possibilities — for example:

x_2 and x_7 were corrupted, and the transmitted word was 1110100;

or x_4 and x_5 were corrupted, and the transmitted word was 1011001;

or x_1 and x_6 were corrupted, and the transmitted word was 0010111;

and so on.

2.8

(a) Yes — for example, the Hamming code of length 31.

A parity check matrix for this code is

$$\begin{bmatrix} 0 & 0 & 0 & 0 & 0 & 0 & 0 & 0 & 0 & 0 & 0 & 0 & 0 & 0 & 0 & 1 & 1 & 1 & 1 & 1 & 1 & 1 & 1 & 1 & 1 & 1 & 1 & 1 & 1 & 1 & 1 \\ 0 & 0 & 0 & 0 & 0 & 0 & 0 & 1 & 1 & 1 & 1 & 1 & 1 & 1 & 1 & 0 & 0 & 0 & 0 & 0 & 0 & 0 & 0 & 1 & 1 & 1 & 1 & 1 & 1 & 1 & 1 \\ 0 & 0 & 0 & 1 & 1 & 1 & 1 & 0 & 0 & 0 & 0 & 1 & 1 & 1 & 1 & 0 & 0 & 0 & 0 & 1 & 1 & 1 & 1 & 0 & 0 & 0 & 0 & 1 & 1 & 1 & 1 \\ 0 & 1 & 1 & 0 & 0 & 1 & 1 & 0 & 0 & 1 & 1 & 0 & 0 & 1 & 1 & 0 & 0 & 1 & 1 & 0 & 0 & 1 & 1 & 0 & 0 & 1 & 1 & 0 & 0 & 1 & 1 \\ 1 & 0 & 1 & 0 & 1 & 0 & 1 & 0 & 1 & 0 & 1 & 0 & 1 & 0 & 1 & 0 & 1 & 0 & 1 & 0 & 1 & 0 & 1 & 0 & 1 & 0 & 1 & 0 & 1 & 0 & 1 \end{bmatrix}$$

(b) No, for such a code would be able to correct up to two errors, by Theorem 1.1. However, $1 + \binom{31}{1} + \binom{31}{2} = 497$, and

$2^{31-23} = 2^8 = 256$, so the Hamming bound is not attained.

Section 3

3.1

(a) Yes — the codewords of this code are obtained by rewriting each codeword $\mathbf{x} = x_1 x_2 x_3 x_4$ of code A as $\mathbf{y} = x_1 x_2 x_4 x_3$.

(b) Yes — the codewords of this code are obtained by rewriting each codeword $\mathbf{x} = x_1 x_2 x_3 x_4 x_5 x_6 x_7$ of code B as $\mathbf{y} = x_7 x_6 x_5 x_2 x_1 x_4 x_3$.

(c) No — code C contains codewords with six 0s (such as 00001100), or six 1s (such as 11011011), whereas this code contains no such codewords; it follows that no rearrangement of codeword bits can change code C into this code.

3.2 The only cyclic code in Exercise 3.1 is the code in part (a):
{0000, 0101, 1010, 1111}.

3.3 As it stands, this code is not cyclic, since $\mathbf{x} = 0011001$ is a codeword but $\mathbf{x}' = 0110010$ is not.

However, if we write each codeword $\mathbf{x} = x_1x_2x_3x_4x_5x_6x_7$ as $\mathbf{y} = x_1x_2x_4x_3x_6x_7x_5$, then we get the equivalent cyclic code

{0110100, 1010001, 0011010, 1101000, 0100011, 1000110, 0001101}.

3.4

(a) For code A, a parity check matrix is $\mathbf{H}_A = \begin{bmatrix} 1 & 0 & 0 & 1 \\ 0 & 1 & 1 & 0 \end{bmatrix}$

To form the dual code we take as codewords all sums of rows of $\mathbf{H}_A$ — namely,

{0 0 0 0, 1 0 0 1, 0 1 1 0, 1 1 1 1}

It follows that code A is self-dual, and that its generator matrix is $\mathbf{H}_A$.

For code B, a parity check matrix is

$$\mathbf{H}_B = \begin{bmatrix} 1 & 1 & 0 & 1 & 0 & 0 & 0 \\ 1 & 1 & 1 & 0 & 1 & 0 & 0 \\ 1 & 0 & 1 & 0 & 0 & 1 & 0 \\ 0 & 1 & 1 & 0 & 0 & 0 & 1 \end{bmatrix}$$

The codewords of the dual code are all sums of rows of $\mathbf{H}_B$ — namely,

{0000000, 1101000, 1110100, 1010010,
0110001, 0011100, 0111010, 1011001,
0100110, 1000101, 1100011, 1001110,
0101101, 0001011, 0010111, 1111111}.

A generator matrix $\mathbf{G}_B$ is the parity check matrix of this dual code — namely,

$$\mathbf{G}_B = \begin{bmatrix} 1 & 0 & 0 & 1 & 1 & 1 & 0 \\ 0 & 1 & 0 & 1 & 1 & 0 & 1 \\ 0 & 0 & 1 & 0 & 1 & 1 & 1 \end{bmatrix}$$

For code C, a parity check matrix is

$$\mathbf{H}_C = \begin{bmatrix} 1 & 1 & 0 & 0 & 0 & 0 & 0 & 0 \\ 1 & 0 & 0 & 0 & 0 & 0 & 1 & 0 \\ 0 & 0 & 0 & 0 & 0 & 0 & 1 & 1 \\ 0 & 0 & 1 & 1 & 1 & 1 & 0 & 0 \end{bmatrix}$$

The codewords of the dual code are all the sums of rows of $\mathbf{H}_C$ — namely,

{00000000, 11000000, 10000010, 00000011,
00111100, 01000010, 11000011, 11111100,
10000001, 10111110, 00111111, 01000001,
01111110, 11111111, 10111101, 01111101}.

A generator matrix $\mathbf{G}_C$ is the parity check matrix of this dual code — namely,

$$\mathbf{G}_C = \begin{bmatrix} 0 & 0 & 1 & 1 & 0 & 0 & 0 & 0 \\ 0 & 0 & 1 & 0 & 1 & 0 & 0 & 0 \\ 0 & 0 & 1 & 0 & 0 & 1 & 0 & 0 \\ 1 & 1 & 0 & 0 & 0 & 0 & 1 & 1 \end{bmatrix}$$

3.5

(a) 0000000 0,   1101001 0,   0101010 1,   1000011 1,

1001100 1,   0100101 1,   1100110 0,   0001111 0,

1110000 1,   0011001 1,   1011010 0,   0110011 0,

0111100 0,   1010101 0,   0010110 1,   1111111 1.

(b) For the original code, $\delta = 3$; for the extended code, $\delta = 4$.

Parity check matrices for the two codes are

$$
\begin{bmatrix}
0 & 0 & 0 & 1 & 1 & 1 & 1 \\
0 & 1 & 1 & 0 & 0 & 1 & 1 \\
1 & 1 & 0 & 0 & 1 & 1 & 0
\end{bmatrix}
\text{ and }
\left[\begin{array}{c|ccccccc}
1 & 1 & 1 & 1 & 1 & 1 & 1 & 1 \\
\hline
0 & 0 & 0 & 0 & 1 & 1 & 1 & 1 \\
0 & 0 & 1 & 1 & 0 & 0 & 1 & 1 \\
0 & 1 & 1 & 0 & 0 & 1 & 1 & 0
\end{array}\right]
$$

3.6

(a) The two codes have codewords

0000 0000	0000 0000
0101 0101	1100 1100
1010 1010	0011 0011
1111 1111	1111 1111
0000 1100	0000 0101
0101 1001	1100 1001
1010 0110	0011 0110
1111 0011 and	1111 1010
0000 0011	0000 1010
0101 0110	1100 0110
1010 1001	0011 1001
1111 1100	1111 0101
0000 1111	0000 1111
0101 1010	1100 0011
1010 0101	0011 1100
1111 0000	1111 0000

(b) In each case, $\delta = \min(4, 2) = 2$.

Taking the parity check matrices of the two codes to be

$$
\mathbf{H}_1 = \begin{bmatrix} 1 & 0 & 1 & 0 \\ 0 & 1 & 0 & 1 \end{bmatrix}
\text{ and } \mathbf{H}_2 = \begin{bmatrix} 1 & 1 & 0 & 0 \\ 0 & 0 & 1 & 1 \end{bmatrix}
$$

and their generator matrices to be

$$
\mathbf{G}_1 = \begin{bmatrix} 1 & 0 & 1 & 0 \\ 0 & 1 & 0 & 1 \end{bmatrix}
\text{ and } \mathbf{G}_2 = \begin{bmatrix} 1 & 1 & 0 & 0 \\ 0 & 0 & 1 & 1 \end{bmatrix}
$$

(since both codes are self-dual), we obtain for the first new code,

$$
\mathbf{H} = \left[\begin{array}{cccc|cccc}
1 & 0 & 1 & 0 & 0 & 0 & 0 & 0 \\
0 & 1 & 0 & 1 & 0 & 0 & 0 & 0 \\
1 & 1 & 0 & 0 & 1 & 1 & 0 & 0 \\
0 & 0 & 1 & 1 & 0 & 0 & 1 & 1
\end{array}\right]
\text{ and } \mathbf{G} = \left[\begin{array}{cccc|cccc}
1 & 0 & 1 & 0 & 1 & 0 & 1 & 0 \\
0 & 1 & 0 & 1 & 0 & 1 & 0 & 1 \\
0 & 0 & 0 & 0 & 1 & 1 & 0 & 0 \\
0 & 0 & 0 & 0 & 0 & 0 & 1 & 1
\end{array}\right]
$$

and for the second new code,

$$
\mathbf{H} = \left[\begin{array}{cccc|cccc}
1 & 1 & 0 & 0 & 0 & 0 & 0 & 0 \\
0 & 0 & 1 & 1 & 0 & 0 & 0 & 0 \\
1 & 0 & 1 & 0 & 1 & 0 & 1 & 0 \\
0 & 1 & 0 & 1 & 0 & 1 & 0 & 1
\end{array}\right]
\text{ and } \mathbf{G} = \left[\begin{array}{cccc|cccc}
1 & 1 & 0 & 0 & 1 & 1 & 0 & 0 \\
0 & 0 & 1 & 1 & 0 & 0 & 1 & 1 \\
0 & 0 & 0 & 0 & 1 & 0 & 1 & 0 \\
0 & 0 & 0 & 0 & 0 & 1 & 0 & 1
\end{array}\right]
$$

using the results of Problem 3.8.

Section 4

4.1

(a) $\mathcal{R}(6)$ has length 64, dimension 7 and minimum distance 32;

   $\mathcal{R}(7)$ has length 128, dimension 8 and minimum distance 64.

(b) By Theorem 1.1, $\mathcal{R}(6)$ detects up to 16 errors and corrects up to 15 errors; $\mathcal{R}(7)$ detects up to 32 errors and corrects up to 31 errors.

4.2

(a) Forming all the possible sums of the rows of the generator matrix (given in the solution to Problem 4.2), we obtain the required 32 codewords of length 16.

(b) We use the $[\mathbf{a} \,|\, \mathbf{a} + \mathbf{b}]$ construction, taking code A as $\mathcal{R}(4)$ and code B as $R(16)$, the 16-fold repetition code.

4.3

(a) Let $\mathbf{G}$ be the first generator matrix for $\mathcal{R}(4)$ given in the solution to Problem 4.2. Then the codewords corresponding to the given messages are

$$[10001]\, \mathbf{G} = [1010101010101010]$$

and

$$[11010]\, \mathbf{G} = [1100110000110011].$$

(b) If the transmitted message is $a_1\, a_2\, a_3\, a_4\, a_5$, then we have

$1 = a_1$	$0 = a_1 + a_2$
$1 = a_1 + a_5$	$1 = a_1 + a_2 + a_5$
$0 = a_1 + a_4$	$0 = a_1 + a_2 + a_4$
$0 = a_1 + a_4 + a_5$	$0 = a_1 + a_2 + a_4 + a_5$
$1 = a_1 + a_3$	$0 = a_1 + a_2 + a_3$
$0 = a_1 + a_3 + a_5$	$0 = a_1 + a_2 + a_3 + a_5$
$1 = a_1 + a_3 + a_4$	$1 = a_1 + a_2 + a_3 + a_4$
$1 = a_1 + a_3 + a_4 + a_5$	$1 = a_1 + a_2 + a_3 + a_4 + a_5$

Comparing the two equations in each row, we get

$a_2 = 0$ (six times) and $a_2 = 1$ (twice).

By majority logic, we assume that $a_2 = 0$.

Similarly, we deduce that $a_3 = 1$, $a_4 = 1$, $a_5 = 0$, $a_1 = 1$.

Thus the intended message is 10110.

Since $[10110]\, \mathbf{G} = [1100001111000011]$, the fifth and ninth bits were corrupted.

Solutions to the problems

Solution 1.1

There are $2^5 = 32$ possible messages of length 5, so the code must contain at least 32 codewords.

Solution 1.2

(a) The code has $4 = 2^2$ codewords, so the dimension is 2.

(b) The code has $4 = 2^2$ codewords, so the dimension is 2.

(c) The code has $8 = 2^3$ codewords, so the dimension is 3.

Solution 1.3

(a) The rates are:

    (a) $2/4 = 1/2$;   (b) $2/4 = 1/2$;   (c) $3/4$.

(b) As there are 2^4 codewords, the code can transmit all messages of 4 bits — that is, it has 4 message bits. Since each codeword has 7 bits, the rate of the code is $4/7$.

Solution 1.4

(a) The encoding rule is not systematic; for example, the message bit 0 does not appear in the corresponding codeword 11.

(b) All three codes have systematic encoding rules:

    (a) This code can be used to transmit all 2-bit messages (00, 01, 10, 11); each message occurs as the first two bits or the last two bits, or the third and second bits, of the appropriate codeword.

    (b) This code can be used to transmit all 2-bit messages (00, 01, 10, 11); each message occurs as the third and second bits of the appropriate codeword.

    (c) This code can be used to transmit all 3-bit messages (000, 001, 010, 011, 100, 101, 110, 111); each message occurs as the first three bits of the appropriate codeword.

Solution 1.5

(a) Each bit of information gives rise to four transmitted bits; the rate of the code $R(4)$ is therefore $1/4$. If one bit of a transmitted codeword is received in error, then three of the four received bits convey the correct message, and so majority-logic decoding yields the intended message. If two errors occur, then only two received bits convey the correct message — in other words, the received word contains two 0s and two 1s — and we cannot decide whether the intended message was 0 or 1. The code $R(4)$ can therefore detect up to two errors and correct one error.

(b) Each bit of information gives rise to five transmitted bits; the rate of the code $R(5)$ is therefore $1/5$. If one or two errors affect a transmitted codeword, then the majority of the received bits convey the intended message. If three errors occur, then the majority of the received bits are incorrect and the message is received in error. The code $R(5)$ can therefore detect and correct up to two errors.

Solution 1.6

(a) 2; (b) 4; (c) 0.

Solution 1.7

(a) (1) $d(\mathbf{x}, \mathbf{y}) = 3$; (2) $d(\mathbf{x}, \mathbf{y}) = 5$.

(b) $d(\mathbf{x}, \mathbf{z}) = 3$; $d(\mathbf{x}, \mathbf{y}) = 4$; $d(\mathbf{y}, \mathbf{z}) = 3$.

Solution 1.8

(a) This code has minimum distance 3.

(b) This code has minimum distance 4.

Here the minimum distances are found by inspection. In Section 2 we see that these two codes are linear and the minimum distances can be found using Theorem 2.1.

Solution 1.9

(a) If one error occurs, then the received word is at Hamming distance 1 from one codeword and at Hamming distance 2 or more from any other codeword. Thus the received word is closer to one codeword than to any other, and so the single error can be detected and corrected. If two or more errors occur, then the received codeword may be closer to a different codeword and the message may be incorrectly interpreted. Thus, the code can detect and correct up to one error.

(b) If one error occurs, then the received word is at Hamming distance 1 from one codeword and at Hamming distance 3 or more from any other codeword. Thus the received word is closer to one codeword than to any other, and so the single error can be detected and corrected. If two errors occur, then the received codeword may be equidistant from two different codewords, and so the two errors can be detected. However, since we cannot determine which is the intended codeword, the two errors cannot be corrected. If three or more errors occur, then the received codeword may be closer to a different codeword, and so the message may be incorrectly interpreted. Thus, the code can detect up to two errors and correct one error.

Solution 1.10

(a) It follows from Theorem 1.1 that a code of minimum distance 5 can detect and correct up to $(5-1)/2 = 2$ errors.

(b) Code (a) has minimum distance 3; it follows from Theorem 1.1 that this code can detect and correct one error.

Code (b) has minimum distance 4; it follows from Theorem 1.1 that this code can detect up to two errors and correct one error.

Solution 1.11

(a) The only codeword at Hamming distance 1 from 100110 is 110110, and the only codeword at Hamming distance 1 from 011001 is 011011. We therefore estimate that 110110 and 011011 were transmitted.

(b) The given code has minimum distance 3, and so can detect and correct one error. The only codeword at Hamming distance 1 from 1110001 is 1110000, and the only codeword at Hamming distance 1 from 0111000 is 0111100. We therefore estimate that 1110000 and 0111100 were transmitted.

(c) The given code has minimum distance 5, and so can detect and correct up to two errors. The only codeword at Hamming distance 2 or less from 1101101110 is 1001001110, and the only codeword at Hamming distance 2 or less from 1111110001 is 0110110001. We therefore estimate that 1001001110 and 0110110001 were transmitted.

Solution 2.1

(a) 1110;   (b) 1101;   (c) 00000.

Solution 2.2

Whenever $\mathbf{x}$ is a binary word with n bits, then modulo 2 arithmetic performed bit by bit yields $\mathbf{x} + \mathbf{x} = \mathbf{0}$, where $\mathbf{0}$ is the n-bit zero word.

Solution 2.3

Code (a) is a linear code; if you add any two codewords, then their sum is also a codeword.

Code (b) is not a linear code; for example, if you add the codewords 0101010 and 1001100, then you obtain 1100110, which is not a codeword.

Solution 2.4

Since $0001111 + 0110101 = 0111010$ and $0001111 + 1100110 = 1101001$, which are missing from the list, two of the other codewords are 0111010 and 1101001. The other missing codeword is the zero word 0000000.

Solution 2.5

(a) Let $\mathbf{z}$ be the binary word with 1s in the places where the bits of $\mathbf{x}$ and $\mathbf{y}$ differ, and 0s in the places where they agree; then $\mathbf{z} = \mathbf{x} + \mathbf{y}$. The Hamming distance between $\mathbf{x}$ and $\mathbf{y}$ is $w(\mathbf{z})$, and so

$$d(\mathbf{x}, \mathbf{y}) = w(\mathbf{z})$$
$$= w(\mathbf{x} + \mathbf{y}).$$

(b) If $\mathbf{z}$ is any codeword, then $w(\mathbf{z}) = d(\mathbf{z},\mathbf{0}) \geq \delta$, since δ is the *minimum* distance of the code. To show that there is actually a codeword with weight δ, we note that, if δ is the minimum distance, then there exist codewords $\mathbf{x}$ and $\mathbf{y}$ for which $d(\mathbf{x}, \mathbf{y}) = \delta$. Let $\mathbf{z}$ be defined as in part (a). Then $w(\mathbf{z}) = d(\mathbf{x}, \mathbf{y}) = \delta$, as required.

Solution 2.6

(a) We saw in Problem 2.5(a) that the weight of $\mathbf{x} + \mathbf{y}$ is equal to the number of places in which the bits of $\mathbf{x}$ and $\mathbf{y}$ differ. Let

> i be the number of places in which $\mathbf{x}$ and $\mathbf{y}$ both have 1,
> j be the number of places where $\mathbf{x}$ has 1 and $\mathbf{y}$ has 0,
> k be the number of places where $\mathbf{x}$ has 0 and $\mathbf{y}$ has 1.

Then $w(\mathbf{x}) = i + j$ and $w(\mathbf{y}) = i + k$, and

$$w(\mathbf{x} + \mathbf{y}) = j + k = (i + j) + (i + k) - 2i \leq w(\mathbf{x}) + w(\mathbf{y}).$$

(b) Applying the triangle inequality for the Hamming distance to the codewords $\mathbf{x}, \mathbf{0}$ and $\mathbf{x} + \mathbf{y}$, we obtain the inequality

$$d(\mathbf{x}, \mathbf{0}) \leq d(\mathbf{x}, \mathbf{x} + \mathbf{y}) + d(\mathbf{x} + \mathbf{y}, \mathbf{0}).$$

But $d(\mathbf{x}, \mathbf{0}) = w(\mathbf{x})$ and $d(\mathbf{x} + \mathbf{y}, \mathbf{0}) = w(\mathbf{x} + \mathbf{y})$;

also,

$$d(\mathbf{x}, \mathbf{x} + \mathbf{y}) \;=\; w(\mathbf{x} + (\mathbf{x} + \mathbf{y})), \text{ by Problem 2.5(a)},$$
$$= w(\mathbf{y}), \text{ since } \mathbf{x} + \mathbf{x} = \mathbf{0}.$$

It follows that

$$w(\mathbf{x}) \leq w(\mathbf{y}) + w(\mathbf{x} + \mathbf{y}),$$

which can be rearranged to give the required result.

Solution 2.7

There are several possibilities — for example,

⟨0011101, 0101011, 1000111⟩ or ⟨1011010, 1101100, 1110001⟩.

Solution 2.8

Again, there are several possibilities — for example:

(a) $\langle 0011, 0101, 1001 \rangle$ or $\langle 1010, 1100, 1111 \rangle$;

(b) $\langle 001110, 100011, 111000 \rangle$ or $\langle 010101, 110110, 111000 \rangle$.

Solution 2.9

In each case, there are several possibilities — for example:

(a)

$$
\begin{bmatrix} 0 & 0 & 0 & 1 & 1 & 1 & 1 \\ 1 & 0 & 1 & 0 & 0 & 1 & 1 \\ 0 & 1 & 1 & 0 & 1 & 0 & 1 \end{bmatrix}
\text{ or }
\begin{bmatrix} 1 & 0 & 1 & 1 & 1 & 0 & 0 \\ 0 & 1 & 1 & 0 & 1 & 0 & 1 \\ 1 & 1 & 0 & 0 & 1 & 1 & 0 \end{bmatrix}
$$

(b)

$$
\begin{bmatrix} 0 & 0 & 1 & 1 \\ 0 & 1 & 0 & 1 \\ 1 & 1 & 1 & 1 \end{bmatrix}
\text{ or }
\begin{bmatrix} 0 & 1 & 1 & 0 \\ 1 & 1 & 0 & 0 \\ 1 & 0 & 0 & 1 \end{bmatrix}
\text{ or }
\begin{bmatrix} 1 & 1 & 1 & 1 \\ 1 & 1 & 0 & 0 \\ 1 & 0 & 1 & 0 \end{bmatrix}
$$

Solution 2.10

(a) In each case, we evaluate the matrix product $\mathbf{mG}$, where $\mathbf{m}$ is the given four-bit message.

(1) $\begin{bmatrix} 1 & 0 & 1 & 1 \end{bmatrix} \begin{bmatrix} 1 & 1 & 1 & 0 & 0 & 0 & 0 \\ 1 & 0 & 0 & 1 & 1 & 0 & 0 \\ 0 & 1 & 0 & 1 & 0 & 1 & 0 \\ 1 & 1 & 0 & 1 & 0 & 0 & 1 \end{bmatrix} = \begin{bmatrix} 0 & 1 & 1 & 0 & 0 & 1 & 1 \end{bmatrix}$

(2) $\begin{bmatrix} 0 & 0 & 0 & 1 \end{bmatrix} \begin{bmatrix} 1 & 1 & 1 & 0 & 0 & 0 & 0 \\ 1 & 0 & 0 & 1 & 1 & 0 & 0 \\ 0 & 1 & 0 & 1 & 0 & 1 & 0 \\ 1 & 1 & 0 & 1 & 0 & 0 & 1 \end{bmatrix} = \begin{bmatrix} 1 & 1 & 0 & 1 & 0 & 0 & 1 \end{bmatrix}$

(3) $\begin{bmatrix} 1 & 1 & 0 & 1 \end{bmatrix} \begin{bmatrix} 1 & 1 & 1 & 0 & 0 & 0 & 0 \\ 1 & 0 & 0 & 1 & 1 & 0 & 0 \\ 0 & 1 & 0 & 1 & 0 & 1 & 0 \\ 1 & 1 & 0 & 1 & 0 & 0 & 1 \end{bmatrix} = \begin{bmatrix} 1 & 0 & 1 & 0 & 1 & 0 & 1 \end{bmatrix}$

(4) $\begin{bmatrix} 0 & 0 & 0 & 0 \end{bmatrix} \begin{bmatrix} 1 & 1 & 1 & 0 & 0 & 0 & 0 \\ 1 & 0 & 0 & 1 & 1 & 0 & 0 \\ 0 & 1 & 0 & 1 & 0 & 1 & 0 \\ 1 & 1 & 0 & 1 & 0 & 0 & 1 \end{bmatrix} = \begin{bmatrix} 0 & 0 & 0 & 0 & 0 & 0 & 0 \end{bmatrix}$

(b) The first bit of each message encoded in part (a) appears as the third bit of its codeword, and the second, third and fourth bits of each codeword appear as the fifth, sixth and seventh bits. Thus we are using a systematic encoder. Columns 3, 5, 6 and 7 are the columns of the 4×4 identity matrix.

Solution 2.11

(a) The error word is 1001000. Adding it to the given codeword yields the received word 1000111.

(b) The error word is 0110001. Adding it to the given codeword yields the received word 0111110.

Solution 2.12

(a) This is a (4, 2) code, and so its parity check matrix is a 2×4 matrix. The bits of each codeword $\mathbf{x}$ satisfy the equations

$$
\begin{aligned}
x_1 \quad\quad + \quad x_3 \quad\quad\quad\quad &= 0 \ (\text{modulo } 2) \\
x_2 \quad\quad\quad + \quad x_4 \quad &= 0 \ (\text{modulo } 2) \\
x_1 \quad + \quad x_2 \quad + \quad x_3 \quad + \quad x_4 \quad &= 0 \ (\text{modulo } 2).
\end{aligned}
$$

We must choose only two of these equations, so three possible parity check matrices are

$$
\begin{bmatrix} 1 & 0 & 1 & 0 \\ 0 & 1 & 0 & 1 \end{bmatrix}, \quad
\begin{bmatrix} 1 & 0 & 1 & 0 \\ 1 & 1 & 1 & 1 \end{bmatrix}, \quad
\begin{bmatrix} 0 & 1 & 0 & 1 \\ 1 & 1 & 1 & 1 \end{bmatrix}
$$

(b) This is a (4, 1) code, and so its parity check matrix is a 3×4 matrix. The bits of each codeword $\mathbf{x}$ satisfy the equations $x_1 = x_2 = x_3 = x_4$, giving the parity check equations

$x_1 + x_2 = 0$ (modulo 2), $\quad\quad x_1 + x_3 = 0$ (modulo 2),

$x_1 + x_4 = 0$ (modulo 2), $\quad\quad x_2 + x_3 = 0$ (modulo 2),

$x_2 + x_4 = 0$ (modulo 2), $\quad\quad x_3 + x_4 = 0$ (modulo 2),

$x_1 + x_2 + x_3 + x_4 = 0$ (modulo 2).

There are several different parity check matrices; the following matrices are three possible candidates:

$$
\begin{bmatrix} 1 & 1 & 0 & 0 \\ 1 & 0 & 1 & 0 \\ 1 & 0 & 0 & 1 \end{bmatrix}, \quad
\begin{bmatrix} 1 & 1 & 0 & 0 \\ 1 & 0 & 1 & 0 \\ 1 & 1 & 1 & 1 \end{bmatrix}, \quad
\begin{bmatrix} 0 & 1 & 1 & 0 \\ 0 & 1 & 0 & 1 \\ 1 & 1 & 1 & 1 \end{bmatrix}
$$

Solution 2.13

(a) The matrix $\mathbf{H}$ is a 1×6 matrix, so we seek a (6, 5) code.

For any codeword $x_1 \, x_2 \, x_3 \, x_4 \, x_5 \, x_6$, the sum $x_1 + x_2 + x_3 + x_4 + x_5 + x_6$ must be even. There are 2^5 words of length 6 whose bits have even sum, and they all must lie in the code. Thus $\mathbf{H}$ is the parity check matrix of the even-weight code of length 6.

(b) The matrix $\mathbf{H}$ is a 4×5 matrix, so we seek a (5, 1) code.

For any codeword $x_1 \, x_2 \, x_3 \, x_4 \, x_5$, we have the parity check equations

$x_1 + x_2 = 0$ (modulo 2), $\quad\quad x_1 + x_3 = 0$ (modulo 2),

$x_1 + x_4 = 0$ (modulo 2), $\quad\quad x_1 + x_5 = 0$ (modulo 2).

It follows that $x_1 = x_2 = x_3 = x_4 = x_5$.

In other words, the code is the five-fold repetition code $R(5)$.

Solution 2.14

We have

$$\mathbf{Hr}^T = \begin{bmatrix} 1 & 0 & 0 & 0 & 0 & 0 & 1 & 0 & 0 & 0 \\ 1 & 1 & 0 & 0 & 0 & 0 & 0 & 1 & 0 & 0 \\ 1 & 1 & 0 & 0 & 0 & 1 & 0 & 0 & 1 & 0 \\ 0 & 1 & 0 & 0 & 0 & 0 & 0 & 0 & 0 & 1 \\ 0 & 0 & 1 & 0 & 0 & 1 & 0 & 0 & 0 & 0 \\ 1 & 0 & 0 & 1 & 0 & 1 & 0 & 0 & 0 & 0 \\ 0 & 1 & 0 & 0 & 1 & 1 & 0 & 0 & 0 & 0 \end{bmatrix} \begin{bmatrix} 0 \\ 1 \\ 0 \\ 1 \\ 1 \\ 0 \\ 0 \\ 0 \\ 1 \\ 1 \end{bmatrix} = \begin{bmatrix} 0 \\ 1 \\ 0 \\ 0 \\ 0 \\ 1 \\ 0 \end{bmatrix}$$

Since $[0100010]^T$ is the sum of the 4th and 8th columns of $\mathbf{H}$, the 4th and 8th bits must have been corrupted. The transmitted codeword was therefore 0100100111.

Solution 2.15

(a) We calculate the syndrome $\mathbf{Hr}^T$ for each received word $\mathbf{r}$, where $\mathbf{H}$ is the parity check matrix

$$\begin{bmatrix} 0 & 0 & 0 & 1 & 1 & 1 & 1 \\ 0 & 1 & 1 & 0 & 0 & 1 & 1 \\ 1 & 0 & 1 & 0 & 1 & 0 & 1 \end{bmatrix}$$

(1) $\mathbf{Hr}^T = \begin{bmatrix} 0 \\ 1 \\ 1 \end{bmatrix}$

so the third bit is in error. We therefore estimate that 1011010 was transmitted.

(2) $\mathbf{Hr}^T = \begin{bmatrix} 1 \\ 1 \\ 1 \end{bmatrix}$

so the seventh bit is in error. We therefore estimate that 1110000 was transmitted.

(3) $\mathbf{Hr}^T = \begin{bmatrix} 1 \\ 0 \\ 1 \end{bmatrix}$

so the fifth bit is in error. We therefore estimate that 0111100 was transmitted.

(b) The codewords obtained by decoding the binary words 1110001 and 0111000 in part (a) using syndromes are the same as those obtained in Problem 1.11(b) where decoding was carried out by direct comparison.

Solution 2.16

Since $15 = 2^4 - 1$, the Hamming code of length 15 has $m = 4$. So $k = 15 - 4 = 11$, and the rate of the code is $11/15$. There are 15 different non-zero columns of length 4; writing them in increasing binary order we obtain the parity check matrix

$$\mathbf{H} = \begin{bmatrix} 0 & 0 & 0 & 0 & 0 & 0 & 0 & 1 & 1 & 1 & 1 & 1 & 1 & 1 & 1 \\ 0 & 0 & 0 & 1 & 1 & 1 & 1 & 0 & 0 & 0 & 0 & 1 & 1 & 1 & 1 \\ 0 & 1 & 1 & 0 & 0 & 1 & 1 & 0 & 0 & 1 & 1 & 0 & 0 & 1 & 1 \\ 1 & 0 & 1 & 0 & 1 & 0 & 1 & 0 & 1 & 0 & 1 & 0 & 1 & 0 & 1 \end{bmatrix}$$

Solution 2.17

(a) No. Such a code could correct up to two errors, by Theorem 1.1, and the Hamming inequality would become

$$1 + \binom{21}{1} + \binom{21}{2} \le 2^{21-14},$$

or $232 \le 128$, which is incorrect.

(b) We cannot say. Such a code could correct up to two errors, by Theorem 1.1, and the Hamming inequality would become

$$1 + \binom{64}{1} + \binom{64}{2} \le 2^{64-51},$$

or $2081 \le 8192$, which is correct. Thus, the Hamming inequality is not violated, but this does not mean that such a code must exist.

(c) No. Such a code could correct up to three errors, by Theorem 1.1, and the Hamming inequality would become

$$1 + \binom{64}{1} + \binom{64}{2} + \binom{64}{3} \le 2^{64-51},$$

or $43745 \le 8192$, which is incorrect.

Solution 2.18

(a) This code is a (6, 3) code that corrects one error. The Hamming inequality is

$$1 + \binom{6}{1} \le 2^{6-3}, \text{ or } 7 \le 8,$$

which is not an equality. Thus, the code is not perfect.

(b) This code is a (4, 1) code that corrects one error. The Hamming inequality is

$$1 + \binom{4}{1} \le 2^{4-1}, \text{ or } 5 \le 8,$$

which is not an equality. Thus, the code is not perfect.

(c) This code is a (5, 1) code that corrects up to two errors. The Hamming inequality is

$$1 + \binom{5}{1} + \binom{5}{2} \le 2^{5-1}, \text{ or } 16 \le 16,$$

which is an equality. Thus, the code is perfect.

Solution 3.1

(a) The codewords of code B are obtained from those of code A by interchanging the first and last bits.

(b) A parity check matrix for code B is obtained by interchanging the first and last columns of a parity check matrix for code A. For example, if we choose

$$\mathbf{H} = \begin{bmatrix} 0 & 1 & 0 & 1 \\ 1 & 1 & 1 & 1 \end{bmatrix}$$

as a parity check matrix for code A, then we obtain

$$\mathbf{K} = \begin{bmatrix} 1 & 1 & 0 & 0 \\ 1 & 1 & 1 & 1 \end{bmatrix}$$

as a parity check matrix for code B.

Solution 3.2

Using the generator set in Section 2.2, we obtain the generator matrix

$$\mathbf{G} = \begin{bmatrix} 1 & 0 & 0 & 0 & 1 & 1 & 1 \\ 0 & 1 & 0 & 1 & 0 & 1 & 1 \\ 0 & 0 & 1 & 1 & 1 & 0 & 1 \end{bmatrix}$$

This is already in standard form, so we do not need to rearrange the columns. The corresponding parity check matrix is

$$\mathbf{H} = \begin{bmatrix} 0 & 1 & 1 & 1 & 0 & 0 & 0 \\ 1 & 0 & 1 & 0 & 1 & 0 & 0 \\ 1 & 1 & 0 & 0 & 0 & 1 & 0 \\ 1 & 1 & 1 & 0 & 0 & 0 & 1 \end{bmatrix}$$

Solution 3.3

Code (a) is cyclic; code (b) is not.

Solution 3.4

Using the definition of a cyclic code, we successively obtain the following codewords:

0011101, 0111010, 1110100, 1101001, 1010011, 0100111.

A parity-check for the (7, 4) cyclic Hamming code is

$$\mathbf{H} = \begin{bmatrix} 1 & 1 & 1 & 0 & 1 & 0 & 0 \\ 0 & 1 & 1 & 1 & 0 & 1 & 0 \\ 0 & 0 & 1 & 1 & 1 & 0 & 1 \end{bmatrix}.$$

Solution 3.5

It follows from the definition of the dual code that $\mathbf{H}$ is the generator matrix of C^*, and hence that the codewords of C^* are obtained by adding rows of $\mathbf{H}$. This gives the codewords

0000, 1010, 0101 and 1111.

Note that, in this case, we obtain the code C with which we started.

A code that is its own dual, such as this one, is called a **self-dual code**.

Solution 3.6

(a) The extended code has minimum distance 6, and so, by Theorem 1.1, it can detect up to three errors and correct up to two errors.

(b) The extended code has minimum distance 8, and so, by Theorem 1.1, it can detect up to four errors and correct up to three errors.

Solution 3.7

Code A is a (4, 3, 2) code, and code B is a (4, 1, 4) code. It follows from Theorem 3.5 that the [a | a + b] construction with codes A and B interchanged results in an (8, 4, 2) code. This code can detect only one error, whereas the code in Example 3.10 can detect up to two errors. The codewords of this new code are as follows.

0000	0 + a	1111	1 + a
0000	0000	1111	1111
0000	0011	1111	1100
0000	0101	1111	1010
0000	0110	1111	1001
0000	1001	1111	0110
0000	1010	1111	0101
0000	1100	1111	0011
0000	1111	1111	0000

Here **0** = 0000 and **1** = 1111.

Solution 3.8

(a) Each codeword in C can be written as the sum of two codewords $[\mathbf{a} \mid \mathbf{a}]$ and $[\mathbf{0} \mid \mathbf{b}]$, where $\mathbf{a}$ is a codeword in A and $\mathbf{b}$ is a codeword in B. Each such binary word can be expressed as a sum of rows of the $(k_A + k_B) \times 2n$ matrix

$$\mathbf{G} = \begin{bmatrix} \mathbf{G}_A & \mathbf{G}_A \\ \mathbf{0} & \mathbf{G}_B \end{bmatrix}$$

There are exactly $2^{k_A + k_B}$ different ways of adding rows of $\mathbf{G}$, and thus $\mathbf{G}$ is a generator matrix for the code C.

(b) Let $[\mathbf{x} \mid \mathbf{y}]$ be a binary word of length $2n$, split into two words of length n. The product $\mathbf{H}[\mathbf{x} \mid \mathbf{y}]^T$ can be written as

$$\begin{bmatrix} \mathbf{H}_A & \mathbf{0} \\ \mathbf{H}_B & \mathbf{H}_B \end{bmatrix} \begin{bmatrix} \mathbf{x}^T \\ \mathbf{y}^T \end{bmatrix} = \begin{bmatrix} \mathbf{H}_A \mathbf{x}^T + \mathbf{0}\mathbf{y}^T \\ \mathbf{H}_B \mathbf{x}^T + \mathbf{H}_B \mathbf{y}^T \end{bmatrix} = \begin{bmatrix} \mathbf{H}_A \mathbf{x}^T \\ \mathbf{H}_B (\mathbf{x} + \mathbf{y})^T \end{bmatrix}$$

It follows that $\mathbf{H}[\mathbf{x} \mid \mathbf{y}]^T$ is equal to $\mathbf{0}$ exactly when $\mathbf{x}$ is a codeword in A and $\mathbf{x} + \mathbf{y}$ is a codeword in B. In other words, $\mathbf{H}[\mathbf{x} \mid \mathbf{y}]^T = \mathbf{0}$ if and only if $\mathbf{x}$ is a codeword in A, and $\mathbf{y} = \mathbf{x} + \mathbf{b}$ for some codeword $\mathbf{b}$ in B. This shows that $\mathbf{H}$ is a parity check matrix for code C.

Alternatively, the matrix product $\mathbf{H}\mathbf{G}^T$ can be written in block form as

$$\begin{bmatrix} \mathbf{H}_A \mathbf{G}_A^T & \mathbf{0} \\ \mathbf{H}_B \mathbf{G}_A^T + \mathbf{H}_B \mathbf{G}_A^T & \mathbf{H}_B \mathbf{G}_B^T \end{bmatrix}$$

It follows from the definitions of $\mathbf{H}_A$, $\mathbf{H}_B$, $\mathbf{G}_A$ and $\mathbf{G}_B$ and modulo 2 arithmetic that this matrix is the zero matrix.

Solution 4.1

The rate of an (n, k) code is k/n, and so the rate of $\mathcal{R}(m)$ is $(m + 1)/2^m$, which quickly becomes small as m increases. This is the penalty for the desirable property that the minimum distance of $\mathcal{R}(m)$ is large compared with the length of the code.

Solution 4.2

The code $\mathcal{R}(4)$ is a $(16, 5, 8)$ code. It therefore has a generator matrix which is a 5×16 matrix, and has rows corresponding to the Boolean functions in four variables 1, v_1, v_2, v_3 and v_4:

	0000	0001	0010	0011	0100	0101	0110	0111	1000	1001	1010	1011	1100	1101	1110	1111
1	1	1	1	1	1	1	1	1	1	1	1	1	1	1	1	1
v_1	0	0	0	0	0	0	0	0	1	1	1	1	1	1	1	1
v_2	0	0	0	0	1	1	1	1	0	0	0	0	1	1	1	1
v_3	0	0	1	1	0	0	1	1	0	0	1	1	0	0	1	1
v_4	0	1	0	1	0	1	0	1	0	1	0	1	0	1	0	1

The ordering of the rows is not important. These five rows arranged in any order from a generator matrix for $\mathcal{R}(4)$. In particular, if we move the row corresponding to v_1 to the bottom, we obtain the given matrix $\mathbf{G}$:

	0000	0001	0010	0011	0100	0101	0110	0111	1000	1001	1010	1011	1100	1101	1110	1111
1	1	1	1	1	1	1	1	1	1	1	1	1	1	1	1	1
v_2	0	0	0	0	1	1	1	1	0	0	0	0	1	1	1	1
v_3	0	0	1	1	0	0	1	1	0	0	1	1	0	0	1	1
v_4	0	1	0	1	0	1	0	1	0	1	0	1	0	1	0	1
v_1	0	0	0	0	0	0	0	0	1	1	1	1	1	1	1	1

Solution 4.3

(a) (1) The codeword corresponding to the message 1101 is

$$[1\,1\,0\,1]\,\mathbf{G} = [1\,0\,1\,0\,0\,1\,0\,1].$$

(2) The codeword corresponding to the message 0110 is

$$[0\,1\,1\,0]\,\mathbf{G} = [0\,0\,1\,1\,1\,1\,0\,0].$$

(3) The codeword corresponding to the message 1000 is

$$[1\,0\,0\,0]\,\mathbf{G} = [1\,1\,1\,1\,1\,1\,1\,1].$$

(b) The message 1000 is not contained in the corresponding codeword 11111111, so the encoding rule using the generator matrix $\mathbf{G}$ is not systematic.

Solution 4.4

(a) Let $\mathbf{a}$ be the message whose corresponding codeword is received as 11010101.

The four votes for the value of a_2 are

$$r_1 + r_5 = 1, \; r_2 + r_6 = 0, \; r_3 + r_7 = 0, \; r_4 + r_8 = 0;$$

we therefore assume that $a_2 = 0$.

The votes for the value of a_3 are

$$r_1 + r_3 = 1, \; r_2 + r_4 = 0, \; r_5 + r_7 = 0, \; r_6 + r_8 = 0;$$

we therefore assume that $a_3 = 0$.

The votes for the value of a_4 are

$$r_1 + r_2 = 0, \; r_3 + r_4 = 1, \; r_5 + r_6 = 1, \; r_7 + r_8 = 1,$$

and thus $a_4 = 1$.

Finally, the votes for the value of a_1 are

$$r_1 = 1, \; r_2 + a_4 = 0, \; r_3 + a_3 = 0, \; r_5 + a_2 = 0,$$

so $a_1 = 0$.

The intended message is therefore $\mathbf{a} = 0001$. The codeword obtained by encoding $\mathbf{a}$ using the generator matrix $\mathbf{G}$ in Example 4.3 is 01010101 — so the first bit of the received word is in error.

(b) Let $\mathbf{a}$ be the message whose corresponding codeword is received as 00110110.

The four votes for the value of a_2 result in a tie, since

$$r_1 + r_5 = 0, \; r_2 + r_6 = 1, \; r_3 + r_7 = 0, \; r_4 + r_8 = 1.$$

We deduce that more than one error has occurred, but we cannot correct them.

(c) The intended message is 1111. Since $[1\,1\,1\,1]\,\mathbf{G} = 10010110$, we conclude that the third bit of the received word is in error.

Solution 4.5

(a) With $G(23)$, 23 coded bits are used to transmit 12 bits of information, so the rate of $G(23)$ is $12/23$.

(b) It follows from Theorem 1.1 that a code with minimum distance 7 can correct up to 3 errors.

(c) This code is a (23, 12) code that corrects up to 3 errors. The Hamming inequality is

$$1 + \binom{23}{1} + \binom{23}{2} + \binom{23}{3} \le 2^{23-12}, \text{ or } 2048 \le 2048,$$

so the Hamming bound is attained. Thus, the code is perfect.

Index